STUDY GUIDE
Ceyhun Ozgur•Sandy Strasser

SIXTH EDITION

BASIC BUSINESS STATISTICS

Concepts and Applications

Mark L. Berenson

David M. Levine

Prentice Hall, Englewood Cliffs, New Jersey 07632

Production Editor: *Joseph F. Tomasso*
Acquisitions Editor: *Diane Peirano*
Manufacturing Buyer: *Ken Clinton*
Cover Designer: *Sue Benke*

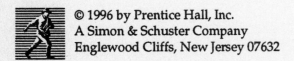

Printed in the United States of America

10 9 8 7 6 5 4 3 2 1

ISBN 0-13-359514-5

Prentice-Hall International (UK) Limited, *London*
Prentice-Hall of Australia Pty. Limited, *Sydney*
Prentice-Hall Canada Inc., *Toronto*
Prentice-Hall Hispanoamericana, S.A., *Mexico*
Prentice-Hall of India Private Limited, *New Delhi*
Prentice-Hall of Japan, Inc., *Tokyo*
Simon & Schuster Asia Pte. Ltd., *Singapore*
Editora Prentice-Hall do Brasil, Ltda., *Rio de Janeiro*

STUDY GUIDE

SIXTH EDITION

BASIC BUSINESS STATISTICS
Concepts and Applications

CONTENTS

PREFACE

The Study guide to Accompany Sixth Edition Basic Business Statistics: Concepts and Applications is a useful supplement for understanding and expanding the concepts and techniques presented in the text. It is not just a review booklet or collection of exercises and their solutions. Its goal is not only to reinforce the concepts and techniques presented in the textbook but also to further develop a sound understanding of the given models. This can be done by emphasizing the assumptions of the various methods so that the students can understand and appreciate the limitations and correctly recognize the possible situations in which these models can be applied.

Each chapter of the study guide corresponds to the same chapter in the text and usually consists of five parts: (1) summary of the chapter; (2) definition and a brief explanation of the key concepts/terms; (3) review questions and their respective answers; (4) multiple choice and fill-in-the blank questions and their solutions; (5) exercises and their complete solutions.

Each chapter of the study guide begins with a chapter summary. In this section, we attempt to provide a concise synopsis of the chapter. Emphasis is placed on the overall usefulness and application of models or techniques presented in the chapter.

The key concepts/terms section lists and defines the major terms and concepts and refers to the section of the textbook in which the concept is covered. When studying the chapter, the student can use this section as a check-list.

The review questions section provides a list of short insightful essay questions to test the knowledge of the student on the basic concepts of the chapter. Sufficient space is provided for the student to write his or her answer.

The multiple choice and fill-in-the blank section provides questions to support the understanding of the basic concepts.

The exercises section provides word problems and other exercises involving calculations. The primary focus of the exercises involves the application of the concepts presented in relevant business situations.

Complete solutions to the <u>review questions</u>, <u>multiple choice questions</u> and <u>exercises</u> are all provided at the end of each chapter .

Appendix A and B are provided as a review of arithmetic, algebra and summation notation. It is recommended that students assess their basic math skills by studying these appendices before attempting the exercises in the study guide.

The study guide and the textbook are designed to complement each other. Therefore, to effectively use this study guide, we strongly recommend that students first read the material in the textbook. Then, the study guide can be used to strengthen the knowledge of concepts presented in the textbook. The study guide would also serve to highlight the ideas, provide the students with an additional opportunity to practice solving problems and give additional examples of analysis and procedures covered in the text.

MINITAB, MYSTAT and DOANE software packages were used in solving many of the problems and exercises in this study guide.

Sandra E. Strasser

Ceyhun O. Ozgur

CHAPTER 1

Introduction

CHAPTER SUMMARY

Statistics involves the gathering, summarizing and analyzing of data to assist in decision making. The collection and analysis of data began as a government function which has spread into many areas and has become an integral part of many disciplines ranging from medicine to architecture. Statistical applications in business extend from a marketing survey of product satisfaction to the measurement of quality in a manufacturing process. The understanding and application of statistics will provide a competitive advantage in the global marketplace of the 90s.

This chapter provides an explanation of modern business statistics, its applications and the importance of statistical computer packages. In the real world, we are usually faced with problems involving large batches of data. Manual calculations become too cumbersome, if not impossible, for accurate and timely solutions. Therefore, it becomes necessary to use the computer to organize summarize, store and analyze large data sets. Another benefit of using the computer is the additional flexibility in data entry, editing and experimenting with potential changes in the data set. There are many statistical packages available. Some of the more popular packages are MINITAB, SAS, SPSS and STATISTIX. The text demonstrates the use of these statistical packages for quantitative and qualitative data and cross-tabulations. It is important to remember that one must have a sound understanding of the statistical concepts to correctly use the computer packages.

KEY CONCEPTS AND TERMS

modern statistics: encompasses the collection, presentation and characterization of information to assist in both the data analysis and the decision-making process. (p. 2)

descriptive statistics: involves the methods of collection, presentation and characterization of a set of data in order to properly describe the various features of that set of data. (p. 3)

2

inferential statistics: involves the methods that make possible the estimation of a characteristic of a population or the making of a decision concerning a population based only on sample results. (p. 3)

population (universe): the totality of items or things under consideration. (p. 3)

sample: the proportion of the population that is selected for analysis. (p. 3)

parameter: a summary measure that is computed to describe a characteristic of an entire population. (p. 3)

statistic: a summary measure that is computed to describe a characteristic from only a sample of the population. (p. 3)

statistical thinking: thought processes that focus on ways to understand, manage, and reduce variation. (p. 4)

enumerative studies: involve decision making regarding a population and/or its characteristics. (p. 5)

analytical studies: involve taking some action on a process to improve performance in the future. (p. 5)

frame: the listing of all the units that belong to the population, providing the basis or the selection of the sample. (p. 5)

REVIEW QUESTIONS

1. Compare descriptive and inferential statistics.

2. Use examples to illustrate the following terms:

    a) population and sample

    b) frame

    c) enumerative study

    d) analytical study

3. Give an example of how statistical thinking can be used to reduce variation in a process.

4. Describe the difference between a parameter and a statistic.

4

MULTIPLE CHOICE AND FILL IN QUESTIONS

1. The two phenomena that led to the growth and development of statistics are
   _____ and _____ .

2. The formulation of the mathematics of the probability theory came from the
   investigation of _____ .

3. Inferential statistics uses _____ statistics to draw conclusions about the true
   _____ parameters.

4. In an analytical study there is no identifiable universe, therefore there is no
   _____ .

5. An _____ study is to parameter estimation as an
   _____ study is to process prediction.

6. _____ is the total of items or things under consideration.
   a) parameter   b) statistic
   c) population   d) sample

7. A descriptive statistic is to the population as an inferential statistic is to the sample.
   a) true   b) false

ANSWERS TO REVIEW QUESTIONS

1. Descriptive statistics assist in presenting and summarizing a data set while
   inferential statistics use sample data to draw conclusions about the population.

2.a) To determine the average salary of professional basketball players, all NBA
   basketball players would be a population. Twenty NBA players could be a sample
   representing the population of all players.
   A population may be defined as all of the windshields delivered from Corning Glass to
   General Motors or all of the tires General Motors receives from Goodrich tire

company. If General Motors inspects 1% of the incoming windshields/tires, this 1% represents a sample.

b) A record of all of the NBA basketball players is a frame.

A listing of all of the windshields and tires received by General Motors in a given shipment represents a frame.

c) Determining the average salary of all NBA players is an enumerative study.

d) Improving the durability of the tires and windshields that General Motors receives over time can be classified as an analytical study.

3. Varying tire thickness will affect durability. In improving the durability of tires, Goodrich could measure the thickness of the rubber so that variation can be reduced.

4. A parameter relates to a population and a statistic relates to a sample.

ANSWERS TO MULTIPLE CHOICE AND FILL IN

1. the needs of government to collect information and the development of the mathematics of probability theory

2. games of chance

3. sample, population

4. frame

5. enumerative, analytical

6. c

7. b (statistics always refer to samples)

6

NOTES

CHAPTER 2

Data Collection

CHAPTER SUMMARY

Chapter 1 stated that statistics involves the gathering, summarizing and analyzing of data to assist in decision making. The gathering of data is a critical first step. If the data are flawed, the summarization and analysis will also be faulty, as these are based on the original data. Flawed data could lead to errors in decision making.

This chapter focuses on the gathering of data. Issues such as the design of a questionnaire, methods of sampling from the population frame and data preparation are all addressed in the context of conducting a real estate survey.

KEY CONCEPTS AND TERMS

data: the numerical information needed to help us make a more informed decision in a particular situation. (p.12)

random variables: phenomena or characteristics which are the events of interest in a survey or experiment. (p. 15)

categorical random variables: yield categorical responses. (p. 15)

numerical random variables: yield numerical responses. (p. 15)

discrete quantitative data: numerical responses that arise from a counting process. (p. 15)

continuous quantitative data: numerical responses that arise from a measuring process. (p. 15)

nominal scale: the classification of qualitative data into distinct categories in which no ordering is implied. (p. 16)

ordinal scale: the classification of qualitative data into distinct categories in which ordering **is** implied. (p. 16)

interval scale: an ordered scale in which the difference between measurements is a meaningful quantity and zero is arbitrarily set. (p. 17)

ratio scale: an ordered scale in which the difference between measurements is a meaningful quantity and there is a true zero point. (p. 17)

operational definition: provides meaning to a concept or variable that can be communicated to other individuals. It is something that has the same meaning yesterday, today and tomorrow to all individuals. (p. 18)

pilot testing: a small-scale version of the study. The questionnaire is given to a small group of subjects to determine response time and possible improvements to the instrument. (p. 22)

non-probability sample: the subjects of the sample are **not** chosen on the basis of known probabilities, but rather on another basis, such as judgment, convenience or a quota. (p. 23)

probability sample: the subjects of the sample are chosen on the basis of known probabilities. (p. 23)

simple random sample: every subject has the same chance of selection as every other subject and the selection of one subject does not affect the chances that any other subject is chosen. (p. 23)

population frame: an up-to-date list of all the individuals or items from which the sample will be drawn. (p. 23)

target population: is the population from which the sample will be drawn. (p. 24)

sampling with replacement: any subject from the target population can appear more than once in the sample. Every individual or item on every draw will always have the same 1 out of N chance of being selected, where N is the population size. (p. 24)

sampling without replacement: subjects cannot be chosen more than once in the sample (i.e., all subjects must be different). (p. 24)

table of random numbers: a series of digits randomly generated and listed in the sequence in which the digits were generated. (p. 25)

missing values: incomplete responses. (p. 31)

coverage error: an error which results from the exclusion of certain groups of subjects from the population listing so that they have no chance of being selected in the sample. (p. 42)

selection bias: if the listing is inadequate because certain groups of subjects in the population were excluded, any sample will provide an estimate of the characteristics of the target population, rather than the actual population. (p. 42)

nonresponse bias: resulting from nonresponse error, the failure to collect data on all subjects in the sample. (p. 43)

sampling error: reflects the chance differences from sample to sample based on the probability of subjects being selected in the particular samples. (p. 43)

measurement error: refers to inaccuracies in the recorded responses that occur because of a weakness in question wording, an interviewer's effect on the respondent, or the effort made by the respondent. (p. 44)

REVIEW QUESTIONS

The owner of a bakery has decided to open a second store and has asked for your help in predicting the demand for baked goods in a particular location. You have decided to design a survey to gather this data.

1. If the bakery owner is only planning to sell to local residents, what is a possible target population?

2. Would you perform a complete census of the population or use statistical sampling procedures? Why?

3. Assuming you could acquire an accurate population frame, what method of sampling would you use and how would you select your sample?

4. Operationally define resident.

5. Develop both a categorical and a numerical question to include in your survey.

6. Discuss the implications of defining the target population as resident families rather than adult residents.

7. Would you choose to do a personal, telephone or mail survey and why?

8. What is wrong with the following operational definition:
   A child's cookie is defined as a cookie that will appeal to children.

9. Explain how selection bias, nonresponse bias, sampling error and measurement error could occur and the effect they would have on your survey results.

MULTIPLE CHOICE AND FILL IN QUESTIONS

1. Gender is a _____ variable while age is a _____ variable.

a) categorical   b) numerical

2. Ford, Chevy, Dodge and Toyota are _____ responses.

a) discrete   b) continuous

c) categorical   d) numerical

3. Five defects were detected in the batch. These defects are examples of _____
_____ _____.

4. The diameter measured 3.5 centimeters. This measure is an example of

_____ _____ _____.

5. Choose the correct measurement scale for the following survey questions:

  i) Do you prefer watching the evening news on CBS, NBC or ABC?

  ii) How much cash do you usually carry with you?

  iii) During December, at what temperature do you set your thermostat?

  iv) What grade of meat do you usually purchase: prime, choice, good or standard?

  v) What is the Blue Book value of the car you currently drive?

    a) nominal scale   b) ordinal scale

    c) interval scale   d) ratio scale

6. A _____ _____ sample ensures that every subject in the target population has
the same chance of being selected as every other subject.

7. If the same subject can appear twice in the same sample, you are sampling without
replacement.

a) true   b) false

8. An interviewer's effect on the respondent can cause _____ _____.

9. A low response rate for a mail survey could be an example of

_____ _____.

10. _____ _____ occurs when the target population is not the same as the actual population of interest.

11. The chance differences from sample to sample is _____ _____.

ANSWERS TO REVIEW QUESTIONS

1. All adult residents within a five-mile radius of the future store could be the target population.

2. A survey is less expensive, more timely, less cumbersome and more efficient than a census.

3. A simple random sample could be used, assigning every resident a random number and using a random number table to select subjects for the survey.

4. A resident could be any person eighteen or over, living in a home or apartment who is located within five miles of the future bakery.

5. categorical - If the bakery is opened, would you shop there?
   numerical - On the average, how many cookies do you eat each week?

6. If families, rather than individuals, form the target population, it becomes necessary to operationally define "family" and to limit subjects in the sample to one per family (if using a simple random sample).

7. Personal and telephone interviews produce higher response rates but cost more than mail surveys. The response mode should be determined by resource constraints of time, money and labor.

8. "Appeal to children" is very general and does not have the same meaning to everyone. The term cookie itself has not been defined. Several items in a bakery could possibly

be called a cookie (crullers, biscuits, tea cakes or Mexican wedding cakes). This definition is ambiguous, as well as, incomplete.

9. If only adults are surveyed, the lack of children's responses would be an example of selection bias. Not receiving many responses could result in nonresponse bias. It is important to determine if those who did respond are "different" from those who did not. In both of these examples, the results of the survey could be misleading because not everyone would be represented. Sampling error is particularly critical when samples are small. For example, if you surveyed only 10 people and by chance they all disliked cookies, this might give you misleading results. Measurement error could occur if you asked those surveyed if they ate cookies, rather than if they would buy cookies. It is possible that someone who eats cookies would prefer to bake them rather than to buy them. This question could give a misleading estimate of purchase demand.

ANSWERS TO MULTIPLE CHOICE AND FILL IN

1. categorical, numerical
2. c
3. discrete numerical data
4. continuous numerical data
5. i) a
   ii) d
   iii) c
   iv) b
   v) d
6. simple random
7. b, you are sampling with replacement
8. measurement error
9. nonresponse bias
10. selection bias
11. sampling error

14

NOTES

CHAPTER 3

Presenting Numerical Data in Tables and Charts

CHAPTER SUMMARY

Large numerical data sets can be efficiently summarized through the use of tables or charts. Patterns and comparisons can more readily be detected and interpreted when the data are viewed graphically. Often data come to us in the form of tables and charts rather than as raw data (with the exception of sports statistics, stock market quotations, and daily weather reports; newspapers and magazines seldom publish raw data). It becomes necessary to summarize and interpret these results without the benefit of all of the data.

This chapter explains how to organize and summarize gathered data into tables and charts. Several methods of presentation are demonstrated for constructing as well as interpreting numerical data.

KEY CONCEPTS AND TERMS

raw form: numerical observations not arranged in any particular order or sequence. (p. 54)

ordered array: a listing of the values in the data set in numerical order from smallest to largest or largest to smallest. (p. 55)

stem and leaf display: separates data entries into "leading digits" and "trailing digits" or leaves. (p. 55)

frequency distribution: a summary table in which the data are arranged into conveniently established numerically ordered class groupings or categories. (p. 62)

class interval: width of the interval of each class grouping where: width of interval = range/number of desired class groupings. (p. 63)

class boundaries: clearly defined class limits (minimum and maximum) for each interval which avoid overlapping of classes. (p. 64)

class midpoint: the point halfway between the boundaries of each class and representative of the data within that class. (p. 65)

relative frequency distribution: formed by dividing the frequencies in each class of the frequency distribution by the total number of observations. (p. 68)

percentage distribution: formed by multiplying each relative frequency or proportion by 100. (p. 68)

histogram: vertical bar charts in which the rectangular bars are constructed at the boundaries of each class. (p. 70)

percentage polygon: formed by letting the midpoint of each class represent the data in that class and then connecting the sequence of midpoints at their respective class percentages. (p. 71)

cumulative percentage distribution table: constructed by recording the lower boundaries of each class and determining the percentage of observations less than each of the stated boundaries. (p. 75)

ogive (cumulative percentage polygon): constructed by plotting the lower boundaries for each class on the horizontal axis (based on the phenomenon of interest) and the cumulative percentages on the vertical axis. (p. 75)

digidot plot: simultaneously presents a stem-and-leaf display and a graph of the observations in the sequential order in which they are obtained. (p. 79)

REVIEW QUESTIONS

1. What is the benefit of placing raw data into an ordered array?

2. Discuss the primary advantage and disadvantage in using a summary table such as a frequency distribution.

3. When analyzing a frequency distribution, why is it almost always desirable to construct the relative frequency distribution or the percentage distribution?

4. When would you prefer to use a percentage polygon rather than a histogram?

5. What is the advantage of using a digidot plot rather than a frequency polygon?

MULTIPLE CHOICE AND FILL IN QUESTIONS

1. The _____ organizes data for further descriptive analysis and prepares the data for tabular and chart form.

2. A frequency distribution should have at least _____ class groupings.

3. It is important that class boundaries be constructed so as to ensure overlapping classes.
a) true   b) false

4. A cumulative frequency distribution is
a) a non-decreasing function.   b) a non-increasing function.

5. If the proportion of observations is plotted on the vertical axis, you are probably looking at a _____ _____ _____.

6. If the percentage of observations is plotted on the vertical axis, you are probably looking at a _____ _____.

EXERCISES

1. The first of the two columns represent random samples of the exam scores on the first statistics exam out of 100 possible points, while the second column represents a different random sample of scores for the final statistics exam out of 200 possible points.

Observation	Exam I	Final Exam
1	86	171
2	68	145
3	97	153
4	76	178
5	48	133
6	71	104
7	82	161
8	60	156
9	76	195
10	91	148

For both samples determine the ordered array.

2. A random sample of class enrollment data in a college of business is given below:

48	30	40	13	32	23	23
15	27	30	25	18	21	33
13	27	21	28	40	24	59

a) place the raw data in an ordered array

b) form the revised stem and leaf display

The following table lists total precipitation in inches during the summer months for each state, by city. Use this table to answer question 3.

State	City	Total Summer Precip. (In.)	State	City	Total Summer Precip. (In.)
Alabama	Birmingham Mobile	13 22	Montana	Billings Great Falls	4 5
Alaska	Juneau	12	Nebraska	Lincoln Omaha	12 13
Arizona	Phoenix Tucson	2 5	Nevada	Las Vegas Reno	1 1
Arkansas	Little Rock	10	NH	Concord	9
California	Los Angeles Sacramento San Diego San Fran.	.07 .20 .13 .20	New Jersey	Atlantic City Newark	12 11
Colorado	Denver	5	New Mexico	Albuquerque	3
Connecticut	Hartford	11	New York	Albany Buffalo New York Rochester Syracuse	9 9 11 8 10
Delaware	Wilmington	11	North Carolina	Charlotte Greensboro Raleigh	12 13 14
DC	Washington	12	ND	Bismarck	8
Florida	Jacksonville Miami Tampa	21 23 23	Ohio	Cincinnati Cleveland Columbus	11 10 11
Georgia	Atlanta	12	Oklahoma	OK City Tulsa	9 11
Hawaii	Honolulu	2	Oregon	Portland	3
Idaho	Boise	1	PA	Harrisburg Philadelphia Pittsburgh	10 12 10
Illinois	Chicago Peoria	10 11	Rhode Island	Providence	9
Indiana	Indianapolis South Bend	11 11	South Carolina	Columbia Greenville	15 12
Iowa	Des Moines	11	South Dakota	Rapid City Sioux Falls	7 15

Continue to next page

Kansas	Wichita	12	Tennessee	Chattanooga	22
				Knoxville	11
				Memphis	10
				Nashville	10
Kentucky	Lexington	12	Texas	Cor. Christi	8
	Louisville	11		Dallas	7
				El Paso	3
				Houston	13
				San Antonio	7
Louisiana	New Orleans	17	Utah	Salt Lake	
	Shreveport	9		City	3
Maine	Portland	8	Vermont	Burlington	11
Maryland	Baltimore	12	Virginia	Norfolk	15
				Richmond	14
MA	Boston	9	Washington	Seattle-Tac.	3
				Spokane	2
Michigan	Detroit	9	West	Charleston	12
	Grand Rapids	9	Virginia	Parkersburg	12
	S. St. Marie	10			
Minnesota	Duluth	12	Wisconsin	Madison	11
	Minneapolis	11		Milwaukee	10
Mississippi	Jackson	11	Wyoming	Cheyenne	6
Missouri	Kansas City	11			
	St. Louis	11			

Rand McNally Road Atlas, 1989

a) Construct a frequency distribution using six class groupings.

TOTAL PRECIPITATION (INCHES)	FREQUENCY TALLIES	FREQUENCY
but less than		
but less than		
but less than		
but less than		
but less than		
but less than		
TOTAL		

b) Complete the relative frequency distribution for total precipitation.

TOTAL PRECIPITATION (INCHES)	PROPORTION OF CITIES
but less than	
but less than	
but less than	
but less than	
but less than	
but less than	
TOTAL	

c) Construct a relative frequency histogram from the data in the table above.

d) Compute the cumulative percentage distribution in the table below.

TOTAL PRECIPITATION (INCHES)	PERCENTAGE OF CITIES IN CLASS INTERVAL	PERCENTAGE OF CITIES "LESS THAN" LOWER BOUNDARY OF CLASS INTERVAL
but less than		
but less than		
but less than		
but less than		
but less than		
but less than		
but less than	0	
TOTAL		-------

e) Construct a cumulative percentage polygon (ogive) from the data in the table above.

f) Why must this data batch on precipitation be considered a sample and not the population?

4. Standard and Poor's Statistical Service (1991) lists the Federal Reserve Bank of New York's discount rates from July 1979 to January 1991. As this data set is time sensitive, construct a digidot plot to determine if a pattern exists over time. Interpret your findings.

Date	Observation Number	Rate	Date	Observation Number	Rate
July 1979	1	10	Apr 1984	19	9
Aug	2	10.5	Nov	20	8.5
Sept	3	11	Dec	21	8
Oct	4	12	May 1985	22	7.5
Feb 1980	5	13	Mar 1986	23	7
May	6	12	Apr	24	6.5
June	7	11	July	25	6
July	8	10	Aug	26	5.5
Sept	9	11	Sept 1987	27	6
Nov	10	12	Aug 1988	28	6.5
Dec	11	14	Feb 1989	29	7
Nov 1981	12	13	Dec	30	7
Dec	13	12	Jan 1991	31	6.5
July 1982	14	11.5			
Aug	15	11			
Oct	16	9.5			
Nov	17	9			
Dec	18	8.5			

24

ANSWERS TO REVIEW QUESTIONS

1. An ordered array allows us to detect extreme values, typical values and concentrations of values. For large data sets, however, it is helpful to organize the data into a stem-and-leaf display.

2. The main advantage of using a summary table is that the major data characteristics become immediately clear to the reader. The primary disadvantage is that we cannot know how the individual values are distributed within a particular class interval without access to the raw data.

3. Conclusions should be made based on relative frequency rather than actual count. Analyzing a frequency distribution requires the additional computation of converting frequencies into proportions or percentages. This step is included in the process of developing a relative frequency or percentage distribution.

4. Several histograms cannot easily be constructed nor interpreted on the same graph. When comparing two or more batches of data, a percentage or relative frequency polygon is easier to construct and interpret.

5. The digidot plot presents the data in sequential order, an important aspect of time series analysis or control charts used in statistical process control.

ANSWERS TO MULTIPLE CHOICE AND FILL IN

1. stem-and-leaf
2. 5
3. b (overlapping classes must be avoided)
4. a
5. relative frequency histogram or polygon
6. percentage histogram or polygon

SOLUTIONS TO EXERCISES

1.   Exam I Ordered array: 48, 60, 68, 71, 76, 76, 82, 86, 91, 97

       Exam II Ordered array: 104, 133, 145, 148, 153, 156, 161, 171, 178, 195

2.

a) ordered array:13, 13, 15, 18, 21, 21, 23, 23, 24, 25, 27, 27,

           28, 30, 30, 32, 33, 40, 40, 48, 59

b) Revised stem and leaf display

    1 | 3358
    2 | 113345778
    3 | 0023
    4 | 008
    5 | 9

3.

a) The range (maximum value - minimum value) is 22.93 (23 - .07) and the desired number of class groupings is six.

    width of interval = range / desired number of class groupings

           = 22.93 / 6 = 3.82   (3.82 is rounded to 4 for convenience)

The smallest value in the data set is .07. For ease in reading and interpreting, set the first lower boundary to zero and the first upper boundary to less than 4.

TOTAL PRECIPITATION (INCHES)	FREQUENCY TALLIES	FREQUENCY
0 but less than **4**	//// //// ////	15
4 but less than **8**	//// ///	8
8 but less than **12**	//// //// //// //// //// //// //// //// ///	43
12 but less than **16**	//// //// //// //// //	22
16 but less than **20**	/	1
20 but less than **24**	////	5
Total		94

b) Complete the relative frequency distribution for total precipitation.

TOTAL PRECIPITATION (INCHES)	PROPORTION OF CITIES
0 but less than **4**	15 / 94 = .16
4 but less than **8**	8 / 94 = .09
8 but less than **12**	43 / 94 = .46
12 but less than **16**	22 / 94 = .23
16 but less than **20**	1 / 94 = .01
20 but less than **24**	5 / 94 = .05
TOTAL	1.00

c) Relative frequency histogram

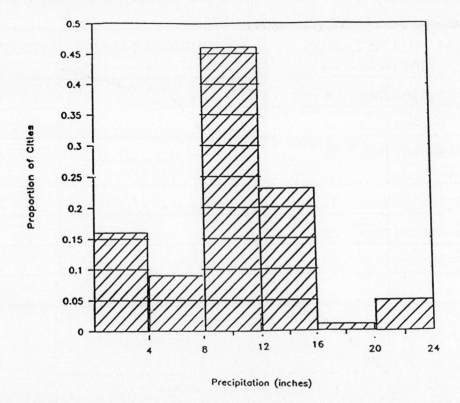

d) Cumulative percentage distribution

TOTAL PRECIPITATION (INCHES)	PERCENTAGE OF CITIES IN CLASS INTERVAL	PERCENTAGE OF CITIES "LESS THAN" LOWER BOUNDARY OF CLASS INTERVAL
0 but less than **4**	16	0
4 but less than **8**	9	16
8 but less than **12**	46	25 = 16 + 9
12 but less than **16**	23	71 = 16 + 9 + 46
16 but less than **20**	1	94 = 16 + 9 + 46 + 23
20 but less than **24**	5	95 = 16 + 9 + 46 + 23 + 1
24 but less than **28**	0	100 = 16 + 9 + 46 + 23 + 1 + 5
TOTAL	100	----------

e) Cumulative percentage polygon (ogive)

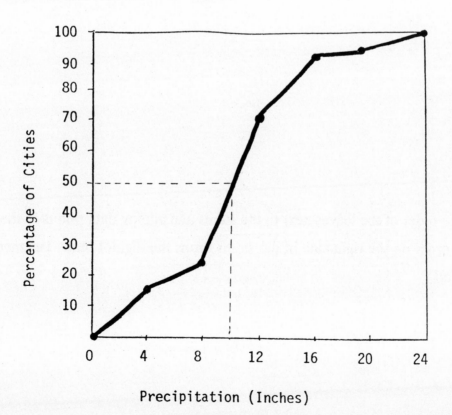

f) In this problem, the population is considered to be all of the cities in each state in the United States. The data for this problem consists of a sample of cities from each state.

4. Begin by sorting the data into an order array

5.5	8.5	11
6	8.5	11.5
6	9	12
6.5	9	12
6.5	9.5	12
6.5	10	12
7	10	13
7	10.5	13
7	11	14
7.5	11	
8	11	n = 31

Using .5 and 0 as trailing digits, the stem and leaf can be constructed. Note, however that the stems are listed from high (on top) to low (on bottom). This differs from the usual stem and leaf which is listed from low (top) to high (bottom).

```
14 | 0
13 | 00
12 | 0000
11 | 00005
10 | 005
 9 | 005
 8 | 055
 7 | 0005
 6 | 00555
 5 | 5
```

Reversing the order of the leaves next to the stems and adding data points in the original (sequential) order on the right side of the stems forms the digidot plot. The median line at 9.5 is added.

```
 0    14                      x
00    13          x           x
0000  12        x x      x x
                         x
50000 11      x   x x    x
 500  10  x          x                    median line = 9.5
 500   9              x x
                      x x
 550   8              x
                       x
5000   7              x      x x
                      x     x  x
55500  6             x x
                     x
   5   5
       0     Observation number
```

A downward trend in discount rates, over time, is revealed in the plot.

NOTES

CHAPTER 4

Summarizing and Describing Numerical Data

CHAPTER SUMMARY

This chapter surveys some of the procedures used to summarize and describe quantitative data. The chapter discusses the three major properties of quantitative data (central tendency, dispersion and shape) and provides ways of measuring these properties. Measures of central tendency give information about the central point of the data set, while measures of dispersion provide insight about the variability of the data set. On the other hand the third property, shape, illustrates the way in which the data points are distributed. Most of the chapter discusses these measures from sample data. The last part of the chapter explains the calculation of the descriptive measures from a population.

In determining the summary measures from a sample, first, a sample is selected from a population, then various measures are used to describe, summarize and organize the sample data. If the sample is randomly selected the statistics are random variables. These sample statistics can then be used as a basis to make inferences about the population. In other words, descriptive statistics not only can provide valuable information about the basic properties of quantitative data (organization, summarization, etc.) but they can also serve as primary sources in drawing conclusions about the population (inferential statistics).

KEY CONCEPTS AND TERMS

raw form: the collected data set is in random sequence with no apparent pattern to the manner in which the individual observations are ordered. (p. 105)

outlier: in a data set, an observation whose value is unusually large or small. (p. 105)

statistic: a descriptive summary measure computed from a sample of data. (p. 106)

parameter: a summary measure computed from an entire population of data. (p. 106)

measure of central tendency: a measure of central point, midpoint or average to describe the entire data set. (p. 106)

arithmetic mean (mean): sum of all the observations in a data set divided by the total number of items involved. (p. 106)

$$\text{sample mean} = \overline{X} = \frac{\sum_{i=1}^{n} X_i}{n}$$

where n = sample size;

    X_i = ith observation of the random variable X

      ordered array: a listing of the values in the data set in numerical order from smallest to largest or largest to smallest. (p. 109)

      median: middle value in an ordered sequence of data (ordered array) (p. 109)

median for a data set with an odd number of observations is given by the following term:

$$\text{median}_{(odd)} = X_{\left(\frac{n+1}{2}\right)}$$

where the subscript (n+1)/2 refers to the position of the observation in the ordered array. The median for a data set with even number of observations is given by the following basic equation:

$$\text{median}_{(even)} = \frac{X_{(n/2)} + X_{\left(\frac{n+2}{2}\right)}}{2}$$

where the subscripts n/2 and (n+2)/2 refer to the position of the observations in the ordered array.

      mode a numerical value that appears most frequently in a batch of data. (p. 111)

      midrange the average of the smallest and largest observations in a batch of data. (p. 111)

The following is the basic equation for **midrange:**

$$\text{Midrange} = \frac{X_{smallest} + X_{largest}}{2}$$

where $X_{smallest}$ is the smallest numerical value in the data set;

    $X_{largest}$ is the largest numerical value in the data set.

      midhinge: the mean of the first and third quartiles in a batch of data. (p. 112)

$$midhinge = \frac{Q_1 + Q_3}{2}$$

where the **first quartile** Q_1 is the value such that 25% of the observations are smaller and 75 % of the observations are larger and **the third quartile** Q_3 is the value such that 75% of the observations are smaller and 25% of the observations are larger.

$$Q_1 = value\ corresponding\ to\ the\ \frac{n + 1}{4}\ ordered\ observation$$

$$Q_3 = value\ corresponding\ to\ the\ \frac{3(n + 1)}{4}\ ordered\ observation$$

variation: the amount of dispersion or "spread" in the data. (p. 118)

measures of variation: five measures discussed include the range, the interquartile range, the variance, the standard deviation, and the coefficient of variation. (p. 118)

range: difference between the largest and the smallest observation in a data set. (p. 118)

interquartile range: the difference between the third and the first quartile in a batch of data. (p. 119)

Interquartile range = Q_3 - Q_1

sample variance: almost the average of squared differences between each of the observations and the mean for a given set of sample data. (p. 120)

The sample variance (S^2) can be expressed as:

$$S^2 = \frac{\sum_{i=1}^{n} (X_i - \overline{X})^2}{n-1}$$

where $\overline{X}$ = sample mean;
  n = sample size;
  X_i = ith value of random variable X.

sample standard deviation: square root of the sample variance. (p. 120) The equation for sample standard deviation (S) is:

$$S = \sqrt{\frac{\sum_{i=1}^{n} (X_i - \overline{X})^2}{n-1}}$$

The following are the computational formulas of sample variance and the sample standard deviation.

$$s^2 = \frac{\sum_{i=1}^{n} X_i^2 - \frac{\left(\sum_{i=1}^{n} X_i\right)^2}{n}}{n-1}$$

$$s = \sqrt{\frac{\sum_{i=1}^{n} X_i^2 - \frac{\left(\sum_{i=1}^{n} X_i\right)^2}{n}}{n-1}}$$

These formulas make it easier and more practical to calculate S^2 and S with hand-held calculators. (p. 123)

coefficient of variation: a relative measure of dispersion given by the ratio of sample standard deviation to sample mean. (p. 125)

$$coefficient\ of\ variation = CV = \left(\frac{S}{\overline{X}}\right)100\%$$

where S is the sample standard deviation;

$\overline{X}$ is the sample mean.

shape: shows the manner in which the data are distributed. (p. 127)

symmetrical data: exact correspondence of the data on both sides of the mean. (p. 127)

skewed data: more observations on either side of the mean which makes the shape of the distribution asymmetrical. (p. 127)

positive or right-skewed distribution: mean > median

negative or left-skewed distribution: mean < median

zero-skewed distribution: mean = median

five number summary: $X_{smallest}$, Q_1, median, Q_3, $X_{largest}$ (p. 128)

box and whisker plot: provides a graphical representation of data through its five number summary. (p. 129)

population measures of central tendency and dispersion: similar to the sample measures except all of the N observations in the population are used. The population mean and population variance are given by the symbols $_X$ and σ^2_X respectively.
The formulas for descriptive population measures are given in the textbook on page 132.

empirical rule: for symmetrical bell shaped (normal) distributions, 68.26% of the observations will be contained within ± 1 standard deviation around the mean, 95.44% and 99.73% of the observations will be included within ± 2 and ± 3 standard deviations around the mean. (p. 138)

Bienaymé-Chebyshev rule: regardless of the shape of the distribution of a batch of data, the percentage of observations that are within k standard deviations of the mean must be at least:

$$\left(1 - \frac{1}{k^2}\right) \quad for \; k > 1$$

Bienaymé-Chebyshev rule provides a lower bound in terms of an observation falling within a given distance about the mean. (pp. 138-139)

modal class: the approximation of the mode from a frequency distribution by choosing the midpoint of the class containing the most observations. (p. 147)

comparing descriptive measures - (group vs. raw data): in most cases, the descriptive statistics based actual raw data does not differ from the descriptive statistics estimated from frequency distribution and ogive plots based on group data. (p. 148)

recognizing and presenting the most proper descriptive summarization: striving to report the most appropriate descriptive summary measures for a given data batch and draw the most appropriate inferences about the population from which the data were gathered. (pp. 155-156)

ethical issues: when making presentations or writing reports or papers about the results of a research study, the results must be given in a fair, neutral way with no willfull intention to distort the truth. (p. 159)

REVIEW QUESTIONS

1. List and define the measures of central tendency.

2. What is the major advantage of using median instead of mean as a measure of central tendency.

3. List and define the measures of dispersion.

4. What is the major difference between the population standard deviation and the sample standard deviation?

5. Carefully compare the empirical rule with the Bienayme´-Chebyshev rule.

6. Why do statisticians use statistics based on samples rather than parameters based on the complete population data?

7. Explain the reasons for using the coefficient of variation as a measure of dispersion.

8. List the five statistics used to develop a box and whisker plot.

9. What is the difference between midrange and midhinge?

MULTIPLE CHOICE AND FILL IN QUESTIONS

1. In statistics, a sample is

a) a measure of central tendency.

b) a measure of dispersion.

c) a complete set of numerical observations.

d) an observed subset of all possible observations.

2. The median may be preferred to other measures of central tendency when

a) the sample size is small.

b) there are outliers.

c) the distribution of the sample values appear to be symmetric.

d) the sample standard deviation is very large.

3. For a given distribution if the mean exceeds the median, then the distribution is

a) symmetric.

b) skewed to the right.

c) skewed to the left.

4. You have learned five basic measures of central tendency. Which one of the following lists gives the order of these measures from the one using the least information to the one using the most information in the sample data.

a) midrange, median, mean

b) median, mean, midhinge

c) mean, median, mode

d) midhinge, mode, midrange

e) midhinge, mean, mode

5. Which of the following measures of dispersion will be influenced the most by an extreme value in the sample data?

a) the standard deviation

b) the range

c) the variance

d) the interquartile range

6. Which one of the following measures of central tendency is affected the least by an extreme data?

a) the mean

b) the midrange

c) the median

Use the following six sample observations to answer the next five questions:

6, 9, 14, 4, 7, 5.

7. The range for this data set is

a) 7   b) 9   c) 10   d)14

8. The mode for this data set is

a) 6   b) 7   c) 6.5   d) there is no mode

9. The median for this data set is

a) 6   b) 6.5   c) 7   d) 7.5   e) 9

10. The midrange for this data set is

a) 10   b) 14   c) 9   d) 7

11. The arithmetic mean for this data set is

a) 7.5   b) 7   c) 6.5   d) 6

12. If a random sample of 9 is selected, then the median will be the fifth value selected.

a) true   b) false

13. The mean and the median will be equal if the data set

a) has a bimodal distribution.

b) has a unimodal distribution.

c) has a symmetric distribution.

d) has a right skewed distribution.

e) has a left skewed distribution.

14. The sample standard deviation measures

a) central tendency.

b) skewness.

c) symmetry.

d) dispersion.

15. The Bienayme´-Chebyshev inequality requires that the shape of the distribution is known

a) true   b) false

16. If the two data sets have the same range:

a) both data sets would have symmetric distributions

b) they would both have equal variances

c) the distance between the highest and the lowest observation would be the same for both
   data sets

d) both distributions would have equal means

17. In left skewed distributions the median is _____ than the midrange.

a) greater   b) less

EXERCISES

1. The first of the two columns represents random samples of the exam scores on the first
   statistics exam out of 100 possible points, while the second column represents a different
   random sample of scores for the final statistics exam out of 200 possible points.

Observation	Exam I	Final Exam
1	86	171
2	68	145
3	97	153
4	76	178
5	48	133
6	71	104
7	82	161
8	60	156
9	76	195
10	91	148

I. For both samples determine the following

a) the ordered array

42

b) the mean

c) the median

d) the mode

e) the range

f) the variance

g) the standard deviation

h) Q_1 and Q_3

i) the midhinge

j) the interquartile range

k) the midrange

l) the coefficient of variation

m) the five number summary

n) the box and whisker plot

o) the percent of observations falling within 1.5 standard deviations of the mean.

p) Based on the Bienaymé-Chebyshev rule, between what two values would we estimate that at least 80% of the data are contained?

2. A random sample of class enrollment data in a college of business administration is given below:

48	30	40	13	32	23	23
15	27	30	25	18	21	33
13	27	21	28	40	24	59

a) calculate the average class size

b) calculate the median class size

c) calculate the modal class size

d) calculate the sample variance

e) calculate the sample standard deviation and the sample range

f) form the stem and leaf display

g) determine the midhinge, midrange and interquartile range

h) determine the five number summary and draw the box and whisker plot.

i) comment on the shape of the distribution

3. Eight samples of 25 items were selected and the number of defectives in each sample tabulated with the following results: 4, 2, 6, 5, 3, 4, 4, 2.

Determine:

(a) the modal number of defectives;

(b) the median number of defectives;

(c) the standard deviation of the number of defectives.

ANSWERS TO REVIEW QUESTIONS

1. mean, median, mode, midrange and midhinge (see the key terms and concepts section for definitions).

2. If an outlier (extreme observation) is present, it is better to use the median instead of the mean. The mean is affected more by the outliers because the numerical value of the outlier is directly considered in its calculation. On the other hand, the median is not affected by the extreme values because we only consider its position in the ordered array, not its numerical value.

3. The measures of dispersion include range, variance, standard deviation, the coefficient of variation and the interquartile range.

4. In calculating the population standard deviation, information about the total population is used. In the calculation of the sample standard deviation, only the sample data is used. This results in a denominator of N (size of the population) for the population standard deviation equation and n-1 (n is the size of the sample) for the sample standard deviation equation.

5. Both the empirical and the Bienayme´-Chebyshev rule evaluates the variability of the data around the mean. The empirical rule assumes a fairly symmetric, mound-shaped distribution and determines the percentage of observations that will be within a certain number of standard deviations around the mean. The Bienayme´-Chebyshev rule applies to any type of distribution. It is used to determine the <u>minimum</u> percentage of values that will be within a certain number of standard deviations around the mean. The empirical rule can be applied with any value for the number of standard deviations around the mean, while the Bienayme´-Chebyshev rule can only be used if the number of standard deviations around the mean (K) is greater than 1.

6. Statisticians rely on statistics because a complete census of the population may be too costly or impossible. For example, it is practically impossible to survey the political opinions of all American adults. Therefore, pollsters will attempt to use a representative random sample. The results obtained from the sample are used to draw conclusions about the population.

7. Coefficient of Variation (CV) is used as a <u>relative</u> measure of dispersion when comparing the variability of two different samples drawn from the respective two populations with different measurement scales. CV is also very useful in comparing the variability of two different populations with the same measurement scale if the means are sufficiently different.

8. $X_{smallest}$, Q_1 (first quartile), median, Q_3 (third quartile), $X_{largest}$

9. Midrange is the mean of the smallest and the largest observations, while midhinge is the mean of the first and third quartile in a given batch of data.

ANSWERS TO MULTIPLE CHOICE

1. d

2. b

3. b

4. a

5. b

6. c

7. c

8. d

9. b

10. c

11. a

12. b

13. c

14. d

15. b

16. c

17. a

SOLUTIONS TO EXERCISES

1.

a)   Exam I
Ordered array: 48, 60, 68, 71, 76, 76, 82, 86, 91, 97

Exam II
Ordered array: 104, 133, 145, 148, 153, 156, 161, 171, 178, 195

b)   Sample mean score of exam 1:

$$\overline{X}_1 = \frac{48+60+68+71+76+76+82+86+91+97}{10} \qquad \overline{X}_1 = \frac{755}{10} = 75.5$$

Sample mean score of final exam:

$$\overline{X}_{final} = \frac{171+145+\ldots\ldots+148}{10} \qquad \overline{X}_{final} = \frac{1544}{10} = 154.4$$

c)

$$Sample\ median\ score\ of\ exam\ 1 = \frac{76+76}{2} = 76$$

$$Sample\ median\ score\ of\ exam\ 2 = \frac{153+156}{2} = 154.5$$

d)   Modal score of exam 1 = 76 (it occurs twice)

There is no modal score of final exam.

e)   Sample range of exam 1 = 97 - 48 = 49 Sample range of exam 2 = 195 - 104 = 91

f) Sample variance of exam 1

X	X^2
86	7396
68	4624
97	9409
76	5776
48	2304
71	5041
82	6724
60	3600
76	5776
91	8281
Total 755	58931

$$s_1^2 = \frac{58931 - \frac{755^2}{10}}{9} = \frac{1928.5}{9} \approx 214.277$$

Sample variance of the final exam

X	X^2
171	29241
145	21025
153	23409
178	31684
133	17689
104	10816
161	25921
156	24336
195	38025
148	21904
Total 1544	244050

$$s_{final}^2 = \frac{244050 - \frac{(1544)^2}{10}}{9} = \frac{5656.4}{9} \approx 628.4889$$

g) The sample standard deviation of the exam 1 scores = s_1

$$s_1 = \sqrt{214.277} \approx 14.6382$$

The sample standard deviation of the final exam scores = s_{final}

$$s_{final} = \sqrt{628.4889} \approx 25.07$$

h) Q_1 and Q_3

$Q_1 = \dfrac{10+1}{4}$ *th ordered observation*

$Q_1 = 2.75$ *third ordered observation*

$Q_3 = \dfrac{3(11)}{4}$ *ordered observation*

$Q_3 = \dfrac{33}{4} = 8.25$ *(8th ordered observation)*

For the first exam, $Q_1 = 68$ For the final exam, $Q_1 = 145$
For the first exam, $Q_3 = 86$ For the final exam, $Q_3 = 171$

i)

For the first exam scores, midhinge $= \dfrac{68+86}{2} = 77$

For the final exam scores, midhinge $= \dfrac{145 + 171}{2} = 158$

j)   For the first exam, the interquartile range $= 86 - 68 = 18$
     For the final exam, the interquartile range $= 171 - 145 = 26$

k)

For the first exam, the midrange $= \dfrac{97+48}{2} = 72.5$

For the final exam, the midrange $= \dfrac{195 + 104}{2} = 149.5$

l)

$$CV_1 = \frac{14.6382}{75.5} * (100) = 19.38\%$$

$$CV_{final} = \frac{25.07}{154.4} * 100 = 16.24\%$$

m)

Five number summary		
	First exam	Final exam
$X_{smallest}$	48	104
Q_1	68	145
median	76	154.5
Q_3	86	171
$X_{largest}$	97	195

n)   Box and Whisker Plot of Exam 1 Scores

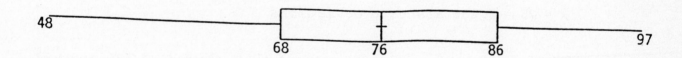

Box and Whisker Plot of the Final Exam Scores

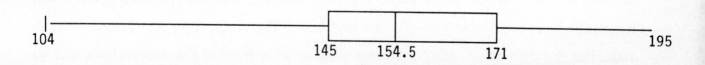

o) First exam:

$$\bar{x} - 1.5s_1 = 75.5 - 1.5(14.6382) = 53.5427$$

$$\bar{x} + 1.5s_1 = 75.5 \mp 1.5(14.6382) = 97.45$$

± 1.5 standard deviation around the mean covers the point range from 53.5427 to 97.45. 9 out of 10 or 90% of the observations fall within 1.5 standard deviations of the mean for the first exam.

Second Exam:

$$\bar{x} \mp 1.5(s_{final}) = 154.4 - 1.5(25.07) = 116.80$$

$$154.4 + 1.5(25.07) = 192.01$$

± 1.5 standard deviation around the mean covers the point range from 116.8 to 192.01. 8 out of 10 or 80% of the observations fall within 1.5 standard deviations of the mean.

p)

$$1 - \frac{1}{(K)^2} = .80$$

$$\frac{1}{K^2} = .2$$

$$.2k^2 = 1$$

$$k^2 = 5$$

$$k = \sqrt{5} = 2.236 \; standard \; deviations$$

At least 80% of the observations must be contained within distances of 2.236 standard deviations around the mean.

For the first exam = 75.5 ± 2.236 (14.6382) = 42.77 to 108.23

For the final exam = 154.4 ± 2.236 (25.07) = 98.363 to 210.46

According to the Bienayme'-Chebyshev rule, at least 80% of the observations will be between 42.7689 and 100. Since 108.23 is greater than the maximum possible points (100), it constitutes an impossible value for the first exam. Therefore, the upper bound is set at 100. For the final exam, using the same rule, at least 80% of the observations will be between 98.343 and 200. (210.46 is an impossible value).

2. a)

$$\bar{x} = \frac{48 + 30 + 40 + \ldots + 59}{21} = \frac{590}{21} = 28.095$$

b)   ordered array:

13, 13, 15, 18, 21, 21, 23, 23, 24, 25, 27, 27, 28, 30, 30, 32, 33, 40, 40, 48, 59

Median is the $11th \frac{(21+1)}{(2)}$ *observation*

Median = 27

c) Modal class sizes are 13, 21, 23, 27, 30, and 40.

d) Variance

X	X²	X	X²	X	X²
48	2304	25	625	59	3481
30	900	18	324		
40	1600	21	441		
13	169	33	1089		
32	1024	13	169		
23	529	27	729		
23	529	21	441		
15	225	28	784		
27	729	40	100		
30	900	24	576		

$$\sum_{i=1}^{n} X_i = 590$$

$$\sum_{i=1}^{n} X_i^2 = 19168$$

$$s_x^2 = \frac{19168 - \frac{(590)^2}{21}}{20}$$

$$s_x^2 = \frac{19168 - 16576.19}{20} = 129.59$$

e) Sample range 59 - 13 = 46

Sample standard deviation $= \sqrt{129.59} = 11.384$

f) Revised stem and leaf display

```
1 |3358
2 |113345778
3 |0023
4 |008
5 |9
```

g) Q_1 is the average of the 5th and 6th ordered observations,

since $(21+1)/4 = 5.5$. Therefore, $Q_1 = (21+21)/2 = 21$.

Q_3 is the average of the 16th and 17th ordered observations,

since $[3(21+1)]/4 = 16.5$. Therefore, $Q_3 = (32+33)/2 = 32.5$.

$$Midhinge = \frac{21 + 32.5}{2} = 26.75$$

$$Midrange = \frac{59 + 13}{2} = 36$$

Interquartile range $= 32.5 - 21 = 11.5$

h) Five number summary

```
    X smallest      13
    Q₁              21
    Median          27
    Q₃            32.5
    X largest       59
```

The Box and Whisker Plot of the class size data

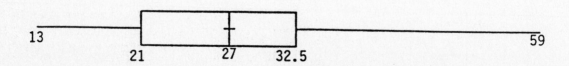

i) The distribution is skewed to the right.

3.
a) Mode = 4 (occurs three times)

b) Ordered array: 2, 2, 3, 4, 4, 4, 5, 6.

$Median = \dfrac{4+4}{2} = 4$

c)

$$\overline{X} = \dfrac{\sum\limits_{i=1}^{8} X_i}{8} = \dfrac{30}{8} = 3.75$$

d) Standard Deviation

X_i	X_i^2
4	16
2	4
6	36
5	25
3	9
4	16
4	16
2	4
$\sum X_i = 30$	$\sum X_i^2 = 126$

$$s_x^2 = \dfrac{126 - \dfrac{(30)^2}{8}}{8 - 1} = \dfrac{126 - 112.5}{7} = 1.9286$$

$$s_x = \sqrt{1.9286} = 1.3887$$

X_i	$X_i - \overline{X}$	$(X_i - \overline{X})^2$
4	.25	.0625
2	-1.75	3.0625
6	+2.25	5.0625
5	+1.25	1.5625
3	-.75	.5625
4	.25	.0625
4	.25	.0625
2	-1.75	3.0625
$\Sigma(X_i - \overline{X})^2 = $ 13.5		

$$s_X^2 = \frac{13.5}{7}$$

$$s_X^2 = 1.9286$$

$$s_X = \sqrt{1.9286} = 1.3887$$

CHAPTER 5

Presenting Categorical Data In Tables And Charts

CHAPTER SUMMARY

While Chapter 3 demonstrated tables and charts for use in organizing numerical data, this chapter addresses the presentation of categorical data. Charts are used for the display of single variables and tables can be used when analyzing two simultaneous variables.

Included in this chapter are bar, pie and dot charts, Pareto diagrams, contingency tables and supertables.

KEY CONCEPTS AND TERMS

bar chart: each category is depicted by a bar, the length of which represents the frequency or percentage of observations falling into a category. (p. 171)

pie chart: each category is depicted by a piece of the pie, the size represents the frequency or percentage of observations falling into a category. (p. 173)

dot chart: each category is depicted by a thin dashed line tipped with a large dot, the length of the line representing the frequency or percentage of observations falling into a category. (p. 173)

Pareto diagram: a special type of vertical bar chart in which the categorical responses are plotted in the descending rank order of their frequencies and combined with a cumulative polygon on the same scale. (p. 176)

contingency table: two-way tables of cross-classification. (p. 180)

supertable: a collection of contingency tables, each having the same column variable and categories. (p. 182)

REVIEW QUESTIONS

1. Explain why all bars in a bar chart should have the same width.

2. How do you choose the appropriate chart?

3. When is the Pareto diagram most useful?

4. To better explore patterns or relationships in a contingency table, what are the various ways in which raw data can be converted?

5. Discuss the advantage of using the supertable.

MULTIPLE CHOICE AND FILL IN QUESTIONS

1. Determine which type of data would be most appropriate for each of the following tables or charts:

i) pie chart   vi) contingency table

ii) digidot plot   vii) dot chart

iii) histogram   viii) supertable

iv) bar chart   ix) frequency distribution

v) Pareto diagram

 a) categorical   b) numerical

2. _____ and _____ can be used when analyzing several categorical variables.

3. The _____ _____ has the ability to flag the "vital few" from the "trivial many".

4. The purpose of graphical presentation is to display data _____ and _____.

EXERCISES

1. Prior to taking the midterm, 135 statistics students were asked how they were studying for the exam. They were to state the one recommendation they would have for future students. After taking the midterm, the following contingency table was developed to analyze the relationship between passing the exam and student study habits. Study habits include studying in groups, doing extra homework, coming in during office hours, rereading the chapter, hiring a tutor and asking questions in class.

STUDENT RECOMMENDATION

Grade	Study Groups	Extra HW	Ofc Hours	Read Chap	Tutor	Class Questions
PASS	10	32	23	15	1	35
FAIL	4	1	8	1	3	2

a) Convert the table to percentages based on the overall total.

STUDENT RECOMMENDATION

Grade	Study Groups	Extra HW	Ofc Hours	Read Chap	Tutor	Class Quest	Total
PASS							
FAIL							
TOTAL							100

b) What percentage of the students passed the midterm?

c) What percentage of students recommended a tutor?

d) Which recommendations appear to be the most helpful?

2. Using the contingency table in Question 1, construct a Pareto diagram to determine which recommendations were suggested most often by the students.

ANSWERS TO REVIEW QUESTIONS

1. As the lengths of the bars vary representing frequency or percentage, the widths remain the same to avoid confusion. If the widths varied, interpretation of the chart would be more difficult.

2. Chart selection should be based on simplicity and clarity. Often, however, selection is dependent upon the aesthetic preferences of the user.

3. The main function of the Pareto diagram is to separate important responses from those that are less critical. When the variables of interest contain many categories, the Pareto diagram is most useful.

4. The raw data can be expressed as a percentage of the overall total, a percentage of the row totals or a percentage of the column totals.

5. The supertable allows line-by-line comparisons for the categories within a particular row variable as well as for the categories among the various row variables.

ANSWERS TO MULTIPLE CHOICE AND FILL IN

1. i) a   vi) a
   ii) b   vii) a
   iii) b   viii) a
   iv) a   ix) b
   v) a

2. contingency table (2 variables), supertable (several variables)

3. Pareto diagram

4. accurately, clearly

SOLUTIONS TO EXERCISES

1.

a) Contingency table converted to percentages

STUDENT RECOMMENDATION

MIDTERM

GRADES	GROUPS	HW	OFC HRS	READ	TUTOR	QUESTIONS	TOTAL
PASS	7.4	23.7	17.0	11.1	.7	25.9	85.8
FAIL	3.0	.7	5.9	.7	2.2	1.5	14.0
TOTAL	10.4	24.4	22.9	11.8	2.9	27.4	99.8[*]

[*] Due to rounding

b) 85.8%

c) 2.9%

d) Doing extra homework problems, coming to office hours, re-reading the chapter and asking questions in class appear to be most helpful. Studying in groups may help, but I would not advise getting a tutor.

2. To create a Pareto diagram from the data contained in the contingency table, you must first construct a vertical bar chart. The vertical axis represents the percentage of students who made each recommendation and the horizontal axis contains the categories of study habits in descending order of importance.

After completing the bar chart portion, a cumulative percentage polygon (ogive) is added, centering the polygon at the midpoint of each category.

From this Pareto diagram, it can be determined which categories of study habits were recommended most often and the cumulative percentages of these categories. This method of analysis is particularly effective for large numbers of categories.

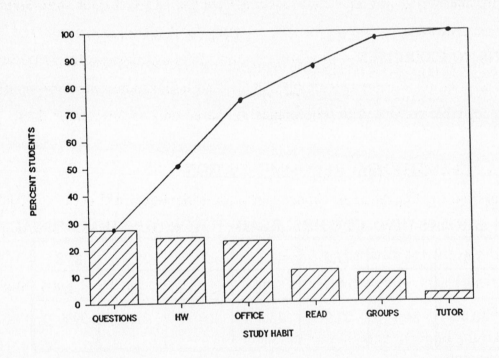

CHAPTER 6

Basic Probability

CHAPTER SUMMARY

Throughout our lives, we are faced with situations that involve uncertainty. When such situations arise, in most cases, it is common to hear the following types of comments in a business environment: "Our chances of exceeding the sales quota for this month are pretty good" or "I doubt that we will be able to receive the shipment before the due date". Probability statements provide better descriptions of uncertainty than the verbal statements given above. We can communicate the language of uncertainty much more clearly using the language of probability. Many times, the statements involving uncertainty are made on the basis of a sample. We can derive different probability statements from a sample. In statistics, the basic concepts of probability will later be used to make inferences about the population from which the sample was drawn.

Probability is an important decision making tool because it provides a formal framework for measuring and analyzing uncertain events. This chapter introduces the terminology and the basic concepts needed to make probability statements and gives examples of applications of basic probability concepts. In later chapters, the results of this chapter will be used to develop specific probability distributions and the concepts will be expanded to draw conclusions about the population based only on the sample data.

KEY CONCEPTS AND TERMS

probability: the likelihood or chance that a particular event will occur. (p. 204)

a priori classical probability: the probability of success is based upon a prior knowledge of the process involved. (p. 204)

empirical classical probability: the probability of success is based upon observed data. (p. 205)

probability of occurrence of an event: X/T

where X = the number of outcomes for which the event we are looking for occurs

T = the total number of possible outcomes (p. 204)

66

subjective probability: the probability of an event occurring is based upon opinions, guesses or hunches. (p. 205)

sample space: the set of all possible outcomes (the collection of all the possible events). (p. 206)

event: a possible type of outcome (occurrence). (p. 206)

simple event: an event described by a single characteristic (outcome). (p. 206)

null event: an event that has no chance of occurring. (p. 204)

complement of an event: given event A, it includes all events not part of event A (Complement of event A is given by the symbol A'). (p. 207)

joint event: an event with two or more characteristics (p. 207).

contingency table: assigning the appropriate events to a table of cross-classifications. (p. 208)

intersection of events: given two events A and B, the intersection contains the sample points belonging to both A and B. (p. 208)

union of events: given two events A and B, the union contains all sample points belonging to A or B. (p. 208)

Venn diagram: graphically represents the various events as unions and intersections. (p. 208)

rules of probability:

a) If A is an event in the sample space, then $0 \leq P(A) \leq 1$

b) The sum of the probabilities for all the possible outcomes in the sample space is equal to 1.

simple (marginal) probability: the probability of occurrence of a simple event. (p. 211)

joint probability: the probability of occurrence of two or more events simultaneously. (p. 212)

mutually exclusive events: events that can not occur jointly or simultaneously. (p. 213)

collectively exhaustive events: a set of events representing all possible outcomes. (p. 213)

If two events are mutually exclusive and collectively exhaustive, one of the events must occur, therefore the sum of the marginal probabilities will add up to one.

addition rule: given event A and event B, the addition rule obtains the probability of event A or event B or both events occurring. (p. 215)

This rule can be expressed using the following formula:

$P(A \cup B) = P(A) + P(B) - P(A \text{ and } B)$

If the event A and event B are mutually exclusive, $P(A \text{ and } B) = 0$ and our addition formula reduces to the following form:

$P(A \cup B) = P(A) + P(B)$

conditional probability: the likelihood that an event will occur given that another event has already occurred. (p. 218)

$$P(A \mid B) = \frac{P(A \text{ and } B)}{P(B)}$$

where $P(A|B)$ = probability of A occurring given event B

$P(A \text{ and } B)$ = joint probability of event A and B

$P(B)$ = marginal probability of event B

From the above equation we can easily solve for the marginal probability:

$P(B) = P(A \text{ and } B)/P(A|B)$

decision tree: displays the possible outcomes and their respective probabilities in a tree diagram. (p. 219)

statistical independence: two events A and B are statistically independent if the occurrence of A does not affect the probability of occurrence of B. (pp. 220-221)

Events A and B are statistically independent if $P(A|B) = P(A)$ or if $P(A \text{ and } B) = P(A) P(B)$.

multiplication rule: the probability of events A and B occurring is the probability of B occurring times the probability of A occurring given that B has already occurred. (p. 222)

The multiplication rule formula for **dependent events** can be stated as follows:

$P(A \text{ and } B) = P(A|B) P(B)$

The multiplication rule for **independent events** is:

$P(A \text{ and } B) = P(A) P(B)$ since $P(A|B) = P(A)$ due to independence.

The earlier defined marginal probability is the sum of the joint probabilities associated with the given event.

Therefore the concept of marginal probability can also be expressed using the following equation:

$P(A) = P(A \text{ and } B_1) + P(A \text{ and } B_2) + P(A \text{ and } B_3) + ... + P(A \text{ and } B_k)$

where B_1, B_2,...,B_k are k mutually exclusive and collectively exhaustive events.

Bayes' theorem: a procedure to revise the conditional probabilities (pp. 225-226) Bayes' theorem is given by the following equation:

$$P(B_i \mid A) = \frac{P(A \mid B_i)\ P(B_i)}{P(A \mid B_1)\ P(B_1) + P(A \mid B_2)\ P(B_2) + ... + P(A \mid B_k)\ P(B_k)}$$

where B_i is the ith event out of k mutually exclusive events.

counting rule 1: If any one of k different, mutually exclusive and collectively exhaustive can occur on each of n trials, the number of possible outcomes is equal to k^n. (p. 230)

counting rule 2: If there are k_1 events in the first trial, k_2 events on the second trial,....., and k_n events in the nth trial, then the number of possible outcomes is (k_1) $(k_2)...(k_n)$. (p. 230)

counting rule 3: The number of ways all n objects can be arranged in order is equal to $n! = n(n-1)(n-2)...(1)$. (p. 230)

permutations (counting rule 4): the number of ways in which a subset of the entire group of objects can be arranged or ordered (sampling is without replacement). (p. 231) The number of arrangements of X objects selected without replacement from n objects is given by:

$$\frac{n!}{(n - X)!}$$

combinations (counting rule 5): the number of ways of selecting X objects without replacement from n objects irrespective of the sequence. (p. 231)

The number of combinations of n objects taken X at a time is:

$$\frac{n!}{X!\,(n - X)!}$$

REVIEW QUESTIONS

1. What is a sample space?

2. Explain the difference between the union of events and the intersection of events.

3. What is an event? List and define the different classification (types) of events.

4. Compare permutations and combinations and give an example for each of these counting techniques.

5. Explain the difference between mutually exclusive and statistically independent events.

MULTIPLE CHOICE AND FILL IN QUESTIONS

1. The number of combinations of 6 items taken 3 at a time is

a) 20.   b) 60.   c) 120.   d) 30.

2. A _____ probability is the sum of _____ probabilities.

a) joint, conditional   b) conditional, joint

c) joint, marginal   d) marginal, joint

3. Three different styles of winter coats are being produced by a company. Style A coat constitutes 25% percent of the total output, while styles B and C are 30% and 45% of the total number of coats respectively. Styles A, B, C have a 15%, 10% and 5% chance of containing a defective item in any given batch. If a coat is found to be defective, what is the probability that it was style C? This problem can be solved by using the

a) multiplication rule.   c) Bayes' theorem.

b) addition rule.   d) joint probability formula.

4. If three employees are waiting to receive their pay checks and the supervisor randomly distributes their checks to all three employees, the probability that <u>exactly</u> two of them will receive the correct check is

a) 1.　　　　　b) 0.　　　　　c) 2/3.　　　　　d) 1/3.

5. Mutually exclusive events are _____ dependent.

a) always　　　　　b) sometimes　　　　　c) never

6. If two events are independent then the probability of their joint occurrence is 0.

a) true　　　　　b) false

7. If two events are not mutually exclusive, then the probability that either event will occur is equal to:

a) the sum of the probabilities that each will occur.

b) the sum of the probabilities that each will occur minus the probability that both will occur.

c) the sum of the probabilities that both will occur minus the product of the probabilities that each will occur.

d) none of the above

8. The probability of two independent events occurring in two trials is equal to

a) the sum of the probabilities of each occurring.

b) the sum of the probabilities that each will occur less the probability that either would occur twice in two trials.

c) the product of the probabilities that each will occur.

d) the sum of the probabilities that each will occur minus the probability both will occur.

e) 0

9. _____ is an ordered arrangement of objects.

a) A permutation　　　　　b) A combination

10. A _____ consists of elements belonging to either of the two sets, A and B or both A and B.

a) complement
b) intersection

c) union
d) sample space

11. A _____ is a number between or including 0 and 1 and measures the likelihood of the occurrence of a given event.

a) statistic
b) sample space

c) permutation
d) probability

12. If P(A)=.6 and P(B)=.3 and P(A ∪ B)=.5, P(A and B)=

a) .9   b) .5   c) .4   d) .6

13. If P(A)=.7 and P(B)=.1 and P(A ∪ B)=.8, then events A and B are

a) statistically independent.   b) mutually exclusive.

c) complements.   d) collectively exhaustive.

14. The number of possible arrangements of three objects selected from three objects where order is important is

a) 9   b) 12 c) 1   d) 0   e) 6

EXERCISES

1. There are 10 players in a tennis tournament. In the singles preliminary competition each player must play a game with every other player. How many games must be played?

2. Employees of the Star Company have been classified by gender and by place of employment.

Gender

Place of employment	Male	Female
Plant	110	10
Office	30	50
Sales	80	20

If an employee is selected randomly, what is the probability that the employee is:

a) male

b) male and works in the office

c) female given that the employee works in the office

d) female or works in the plant

3. A race driver uses model A cars 50% of the time, the model B cars 30% of the time and model C cars 20% of the time. Based on past races, he won .4 of the races when he was driving model A, .33 of the races when he was driving model B, and 10% of the races when he was driving model C. If he has just won a race, what is the probability that the car he was using was model C?

4. The 700 employees of a company are classified according to their opinion of a certain company policy and their job within the company. Results are given in the following contingency table.

Opinion	Management	Clerical	Technical	Totals
Favor	40	120	300	460
Don't favor	60	80	100	240
Totals	100	200	400	700

If an employee is selected at random, what is the probability that the employee:

a) does not favor the policy?

b) favors the policy and is from management?

c) is a technical worker given that he/she favors the policy?

d) is a clerical worker or does not favor the policy?

5. How many two digit numbers can be formed from the digits 1, 4, 5, 6, 9 if a digit can not appear more than once in a number?

6. In a shipment of 20 soccer balls, there are two defective balls. If two balls are selected randomly, what is the probability that one will be defective and one will not be defective?

7. If 80% of the households in Norka have lawn mowers, 40% have snow blowers and 30% have both, what proportion of households do not have either lawn mowers or snow blowers?

8. The NCAA soccer committee is in the process of planning the national championship game sites for division I soccer for 1995 through 1998. If the NCAA wants to arrange the following applicant schools such that each school hosts the championship once. The applicant schools are University of North Carolina at Chapel Hill, University of Virginia, University of Akron and University of Southern California. How many different ways can NCAA arrange the championship game sites?

9. There are five jobs waiting to be processed at a given machine center. How many total different sequences of processing these jobs are possible?

10. If a coin is tossed five times, what is the total number of possible outcomes?

11. If a die is rolled five times, what is the total number of possible outcomes?

12. Discuss the differences in your answers to exercises 11 and 12.

13. A local bank serves five regions, within each region, there are three states, each state is divided into three districts and each district contains 2 branches. What is the total number of branches?

ANSWERS TO REVIEW QUESTIONS

1. A sample space is the set of all possible observations.

2. Given event A and event B, the union contains all of the outcomes belonging to A, all of the outcomes belonging to B and all of the outcomes that belong to both A and B. The intersection of events A and B includes only the outcomes belonging to event A and event B. The term "or" usually refers to union, while the term "and" usually identifies an intersection of two events.

3. The term "event" refers to each possible outcome. The different classifications of events discussed in the chapter include: simple event, joint event, complement of an event, mutually exclusive events, collectively exhaustive events, intersection of two or more events, union of two or more events, statistically independent events and statistically dependent events.

4. Both permutations and combinations involve selecting X objects from n objects. However, a permutation gives the number of arrangements (the order is important) of X objects from n objects, while a combination provides the number of ways of selecting X objects from n objects without regard to the order.

   Permutation example: A small department store has three display windows. In each window one dress is displayed. The store owner has five dresses she is considering to display. How many arrangements are possible? (Answer: 60 possible arrangements)

   Combination example: The NYU basketball team has five players who can play the guard position. The coach will only use two guards at a time. How many different combinations of guards are available to the coach? (Answer: 10 possible combinations)

5. Two events with nonzero probabilities can not be both mutually exclusive and statistically independent. If one mutually exclusive event is known to have occurred, the probability of the other event occurring is reduced to zero. Thus they can not be independent. In using the notation given in the textbook, if event A and B are mutually exclusive, by definition of mutually exclusive $P(A|B) = 0$. Since the definition of statistically independent events requires that $P(A|B) = P(A)$, we can conclude that the mutually exclusive events are always dependent.

ANSWERS TO MULTIPLE CHOICE AND FILL IN

1. a	8. c
2. d	9. a
3. c	10. c
4. b	11. d
5. a	12. c
6. b	13. b
7. b	14. e

SOLUTIONS TO EXERCISES

1. The question is asking for the number of <u>combinations</u> of pairs to be selected. Therefore we use the combination formula.

$$C_2^{10} = \frac{10!}{2!\,(10-2)!} = \frac{10 * 9 * 8!}{2 * 8!} = 45$$

2. Let M = male, F = female, P = employed at the plant,

   O = employed at the office, S = employed in the sales department.

a) P(M) = P(M and P) + P(M and O) + P(M and S)

   P(M) = (110/300) + (30/300)   + (80/300) = 220/300

b) P(M and O) = 30/300

c) P(F|O) = 50/80 or P(F and O)/P(O) = (50/300) ÷ (80/300) = 50/80

d) P(F ∪ P) = P(F) + P(P) - P(F and P) = 80/300 + 120/300 - 10/300

   P(F ∪ P) = 190/300.

3. $P(M_A)$ = .5 $P(M_B)$ = .3 $P(M_C)$ = .2

   $P(W\,|M_A)$ = .40   P(W | M_B} = .33   P(W | M_C) = .10

$$P(M_C \mid W) = \frac{(.10)\,(.2)}{(.10)\,(0.2) + (.05)\,(.40) + (.3)\,(.33)}$$

$P(M_C \mid W)$ = .0627

4.

a) 240/700 = .343

b) $40/700 = .0571$

c) $300/460 = .652$

d) P(Clerical ∪ does not favor) = $(200/700) + (240/700) - (80/700)$

  P(Clerical ∪ does not favor) = $360/700 = .5143$

5. Since the sequence is an important consideration, we need to use the permutation formula.

$$P_2^5 = \frac{5!}{(5-2)!} = 20$$

6. There are two ways of getting one defective and one non-defective soccer balls. That is: (1) the first ball selected may be defective and the second one may be non defective; (2) the second one may be defective and the first one may be good.

   Let N = nondefective ball and D = defective ball.

   P(N and D) = $(18/20)*(2/19) = 9/95$

   P(D and N) = $(2/20)*(18/19) = 9/95$

   Therefore, the probability of getting one defective and one nondefective ball is $(9/95) + (9/95) = 18/95$.

7. The proportion of the houses having either a lawn mower or a snow blower can be found by using the basic addition rule of probability. Let S = having a snow blower and L = having a lawn mower.

   P(S ∪ L) = P(S) + P(L) - P(L and S) = $.8 + .4 - .3 = .9$

   Therefore, the probability that the house in Norka has neither a snow blower nor a lawn mower is given by the complement of

   P(S ∪ L) or P(S ∪ L)' = $1 - .9 = .1$.

8. Since there are four sites and four years, applying counting rule 3:

   n! = $4! = 4.3.2.1 = 24$ possible arrangements. Note that the same solution can also be obtained using counting rule 4.

9. Applying counting rule 3: n! = $5! = 5.4.3.2.1 = 120$ possible sequences.

10. Applying counting rule 1 $k^n = 2^5 = 32$.

11. Applying counting rule 1 $k^n = 6^5 = 7776$.

12. Even though there are five trials in both exercise 10 and exercise 11, There are only two mutually exclusive events (head and a tail) in tossing a coin and six mutually exclusive events in rolling a dice. In other words there are six possibilities at each trial for the dice experiment and only two possibilities at each trial for the coin experiment, resulting in a much larger total possible number of outcomes for the dice experiment.

13. Applying counting rule 2 $(k_1)(k_2)(k_3)(k_4) = (5)(3)(3)(2) = 90$ (90 branches).

CHAPTER 7

Some Important Discrete Probability Distributions

CHAPTER SUMMARY

This chapter builds on and expands the coverage of chapter 6. It illustrates the practical applications of probability as a decision-making tool. In this chapter only the probability distributions of discrete random variables are considered. A probability distribution applicable to many continuous random variables will be covered in the next chapter. Chapter 7 provides a general coverage of discrete probability distributions and discusses the expected value, variance and standard deviation of discrete random variables. This introduction provides the foundation for the coverage in the remainder of the chapter where specific discrete probability distributions are discussed. The two discrete probability distributions covered are: the binomial and the Poisson. In addition, the chapter shows when and how the Poisson distribution can be used to approximate the binomial distribution. The probability distributions covered in this chapter are considered to be very important because they are extensively used in the business world. They also lend themselves to numerous applications in various other disciplines. Special formulas and tables are available to make their use easier for the decision-maker. The chapter provides a clear, detailed explanation of how, when, and in what context these formulas and tables are used.

KEY CONCEPTS AND TERMS

probability distribution for a discrete random variable: a mutually exclusive listing of all possible numerical outcomes for the random variable such that a particular probability of occurrence is associated with each outcome. (p. 242)

expected value of a discrete random variable: may be considered as the weighted average over all possible outcomes, where the weights are the probabilities associated with each of the outcomes. (p. 244)

The expected value of a random variable is given by the following equation:

$$\mu_x = E(X) = \sum_{i=1}^{N} X_i \, P(X_i)$$

where X_i = the ith outcome of the discrete random variable X;

$P(X_i)$ = the probability of occurrence of the ith outcome of X;

N = the total number of possible outcomes;

x = expected value of the discrete random variable X.

variance of a discrete random variable (σ_x^2): the weighted average of the squared differences between each possible outcome and the mean. (The weights are the probabilities of each of the respective outcomes) (p. 245)

$$\sigma_X^2 = \sum_{i=1}^{N} (X_i - \mu_X)^2 \, P(X_i)$$

standard deviation of a discrete random variable (σ_x): square root of the variance. (p. 245)

$$\sigma_X = \sqrt{\sum_{i=1}^{N} (X_i - \mu_X)^2 \, P(X_i)}$$

The variables have already been defined above.

expected monetary value (EMV): indicates the average profit that would be gained if a particular strategy were selected in a given decision-making situation. (p. 246)

The expected monetary value for a particular strategy is given by the following equation:

$$\mu_x = E(X) = \sum_{i=1}^{N} X_i \, P(X_i)$$

where V_i = dollar value associated with the ith outcome of the discrete random variable X;

$P(X_i)$ = the probability of occurrence of the ith outcome of X;

N = the total number of possible outcomes;

EMV = expected monetary value of discrete random variable X.

model: a miniature representation of some underlying phenomenon. (p. 251)

mathematical model: a mathematical expression representing some underlying phenomenon. (p. 251)

uniform distribution: all outcomes of the random variable are equally likely to occur. In other words, the probability of occurrence of each event is uniformly distributed over all possible events. (p. 251)

sampling with replacement: in each trial, a selected item is returned to the total possible set of items available and may be selected again later. (p. 252)

sampling without replacement: once selected, an item is not considered for another selection among the total possible set of items in a future trial. This type of sampling procedure reduces the size of the population in each trial. (p. 252)

major properties of the binomial distribution:

1. sampling is with replacement from a finite population or without replacement from an infinite population.

2. each observation is classified into one of two mutually exclusive and collectively exhaustive categories, usually called success and failure.

3. The probability of success (p) and the probability of failure (1-p) are constant from trial to trial.

4. outcomes of trials are independent of each other.

The following mathematical expression of the binomial probability distribution represents the probability that the discrete random variable X will assume the value of x:

$$P(X=x \mid n,p) = \frac{n!}{x!\,(n-x)!}\, p^{x}(1-p)^{n-x}$$

where n = sample size

    p = probability of success

  1-p = probability of failure

    x = number of successes

 n-x = number of failures

shape of the binomial distribution: as p approaches .5 and n gets larger, the distribution approaches a symmetric shape. (p. 257)

The mean, variance and standard deviation of the binomial distribution can easily be calculated using the following formulas.

$mean = \mu_X = E(X) = np$

$variance = \sigma_X^2 = np(1-p)$

$standard\ deviation = \sigma_X = \sqrt{np(1-p)}$

Poisson process: represented by a discrete random variable -- number of successes per unit (per interval of time, length, etc.). (p. 260)

major properties of Poisson distribution:

1. the interval in question can be divided into many smaller subintervals.

2. the probability of observing two or more occurrences of a success in a sufficiently small interval or subinterval is zero.

3. the probability of occurrence of a success in one interval does not affect the probability of occurrences of success in any other interval (statistical independence).

The following mathematical expression of the Poisson probability distribution represents the probability of obtaining X successes given λ (expected number of successes in a specified interval).

$$P(X=x \mid \lambda) = \frac{e^{-\lambda}\lambda^x}{x!}$$

where x = number of successes per unit interval

e = mathematical constant approximated by 2.71828

The Poisson distribution is unique such that its mean and variance are equal:

$$\mu_X = \sigma_X^2$$

the Poisson distribution as an approximation to the binomial distribution: may be used when n is large (≥ 20) and p or is very small ($\leq .05$). (p. 264)

Note:

$$\mu_X = \sigma_X^2 = np$$

The following mathematical expression for the Poisson model may be used to approximate the true binomial probability.

$$P(X = x \mid n,p) \approx \frac{e^{-np} (np)^x}{x!}$$

REVIEW QUESTIONS

1. To use the binomial distribution, when the population is finite, why is it necessary that the sampling be with replacement?

2. When is it appropriate to approximate the binomial with Poisson distribution?

3. What is a mathematical model and why is it important?

MULTIPLE CHOICE AND FILL IN QUESTIONS

1. A restaurant owner is studying the arrival patterns of her customers. The average number of arrivals per hour is 25. Assuming that each arrival is independent, which one of the following distributions is appropriate for estimating the probability of having 30 or more arrivals in an hour?

a) the binomial   b) the Poisson

2. The distribution whose mean is always equal to its variance is the _____ .

3. The requirement that the probability of success remains constant from trial to trial is a property of the _____ distribution.

4. If ships arrive at a loading dock according to a Poisson distribution with a mean of three per hour, then in a nine hour day one would expect _____ ships to arrive.

a) 27   b) 24   c) 3   d) 2   e) 1

5. Which one of the following distributions should be used to determine the probability of finding 2 defectives from a sample of 45, when it is known that the probability of a single unit being defective is .10.

a) the binomial   b) the Poisson

6. Which one of the following is not an assumption required for the binomial distribution?
a) each trial has two possible outcomes
b) sampling is without replacement from an infinite population
c) two successive trials are statistically dependent
d) the probability of success is the same in every trial

7. The probability of receiving 2 heads in four tosses of a fair coin can be determined by using the
a) Poisson.   b) binomial.   c) uniform.

8. One of the essential characteristics of the _____ distribution is that all outcomes are equally likely to occur.

a) Poisson   b) uniform   c) binomial

9. The expected value of a discrete random variable is called its

a) median.   b) central tendency.

c) mode.   d) mean.

10. The expression $p^x (1-p)^{n-x}$ in the binomial formula refers to

a) the number of sequences with x successes in n trials.

b) the probability of one sequence with n-x successes in n trials.

c) the number of sequences with n-x successes in n trials.

d) the probability of one sequence with x successes in n trials.

11. Poisson distribution can be used to approximate the binomial distribution if p is small ($p \le .05$) and n is large ($n \ge 20$).

a) true   b) false

EXERCISES

1. The mean number of calls received in the customer service department of XNC Inc. is 3 per hour.

a) What is the probability that 5 or more calls will be received in a given hour ?

b) What is the probability of receiving fewer than 3 calls in an half hour period?

c) What is the probability that no more than 7 calls will be received in a two hour period?

d) What is the standard deviation of the number of calls for a two hour period?

2. In the city of Konda, 40% of the workforce is employed by manufacturing firms. If a sample of 10 people are selected from the workforce, what is the probability that

a) exactly four of them are working for manufacturing firms? **(do not use the tables)**

b) three or more are working for manufacturing firms?

c) fewer than two are working for manufacturing firms?

d) more than one is **not** working for a manufacturing firm?

3. The historical data shows that a particular customer service clerk makes an average of two data entry errors per page when entering the customer order data to the computer system. Determine the probability that the clerk will make:

a) a total of seven data entry errors on four pages of customer order data?

(Do not use the tables)

b) at least four data entry errors on three pages of customer order data that the clerk entered this morning?

4. The ENKA inc. buys locknuts from a German supplier. The historical data shows that a lot consists of 5% defective units. The ENKA inc. has just received a lot.

a) If the quality control (QC) staff randomly selects 8 items, what is the probability that they will find one defective locknut in the sample? **(do not use the table)**

b) What is the mean and standard deviation of the number of defectives for part a?

c) If the QC personnel randomly selects 20 items, what is the probability that 2 or more defectives will be found?

5) For the following discrete probability distribution, determine the value of the parameters requested.

X	p(X)
10	.10
20	.30
30	.40
40	.20

a) mean

b) variance and the standard deviation

6. The 26 letters in an alphabet (A through Z) constitute the sample space. If X is the outcome associated with selecting a letter with replacement from the pool of 26 letters;

a) Which specific discrete probability distribution characterizes the distribution of X.

b) What is the probability of selecting the letter X?

7. Let X be the number of hours of changeover time between products in a manufacturing process. The probability distribution for X is $p(X = x) = x/15$ $x = 1,2,3,4,5$.

a) Verify that $p(X=x)$ is a probability function.

b) What is the probability that the changeover time between products will be exactly 2 hours?

c) What is the probability that it will take at least one hour but no more than three hours to complete the changeover between two products?

d) What is the probability that the changeover time is at least three hours?

e) What is the average changeover time?

f) What is the standard deviation of the changeover times?

8. A newspaper stand owner in Akron, Ohio has just purchased 6 units of a certain weekly news magazine. He hopes that he will sell all six magazines before the end of the week. However, the probability distribution of him selling the magazines along with the expected net profit associated with the sales is given in the following table.

Number of magazines sold	Probability of Selling	Profit from selling ($)
0	.05	-2.4
1	.10	-1.5
2	.10	-.60
3	.15	.30
4	.20	1.20
5	.25	2.10
6	.15	3.00

a) On the average how many magazines can the owner expect to sell?

b) What is the standard deviation of the number of units sold?

c) If he continues to purchase 6 magazines per week, in the long run, how much profit can he average?

9. A company produces an average of 1% defective units. In one week, the factory produced a total of 1000 units.

a) What is the probability that 7 of the 1000 units were defective?

b) What is the probability that no more than 5 units were defective?

c) What is the probability that more than 12 units were defective?

ANSWERS TO REVIEW QUESTIONS

1. Sampling with replacement ensures that the probability of success remains constant from trial to trial (one of the major properties of the binomial distribution). Otherwise, if sampling is done without replacement, the probability of success will be affected by the outcome of the previous trials (observations).

2. It is appropriate to approximate the binomial using the Poisson distribution when n is very large and p is very small.

94

3. A mathematical model is a mathematical expression representing some underlying phenomenon. A model is designed to merely capture the essential features of reality. A model is important because it can enable the discovery of a relationship between two or more variables and, more importantly, a solution to a model can provide valuable assistance to the decision-maker.

ANSWERS TO MULTIPLE CHOICE AND FILL IN

1. b	6. c
2. Poisson	7. b
3. Binomial	8. b
4. a	9. d
5. a	10. d
11. a	

SOLUTIONS TO EXERCISES

1. a) λ = 3 calls per hour

$1-P(X \leq 4 | \lambda = 3) = 1-[P(X=4)+P(X=3)+P(X=2)+P(X=1)+P(X=0)]$ using table E.6.

$1-P(X \leq 4) = 1-(.168 + .224 + .224 + .1494 + .0498) = .1848$

b) λ = 1.5 calls per half hour

$P(X \leq 2 | \lambda = 1.5) = P(X=2)+P(X=1)+P(X=0)$

$P(X \leq 2 | \lambda = 1.5) = .2231^* + .3347 + .2510 = .8088$

* The individual probabilities are obtained from table E.6.

c) λ = 6 calls per 2 hours

$P(X \leq 7 | \lambda = 6) = P(X=7)+P(X=6)+......+P(X=1)+P(X=0)$

$P(X \leq 7 | \lambda = 6) = .1377 + .1606 +.....+ .0149 + .0025$

$P(X \leq 7 | \lambda = 6) = .7440$

d) the standard deviation of the number of calls for two hours = σ_x

$\sigma_x = \sqrt{\lambda} = \sqrt{6} \approx 2.4495$

2. a)

$$P(X=4 \mid n=10,p=.4) = \binom{10}{4}(.4)^4(.6)^6 = \frac{10!}{4! \; 6!}(.0256)(.0467)$$

$P(X=4|n=10,p=.4) = .2508$

b) $P(X \geq 3|n=10,p=.4) = 1 - P(X \leq 2|n=10,p=.4)$

$\quad P(X \geq 3|n=10,p=.4) = 1 - P(X=2)+P(X=1)+P(X=0)$

$\quad P(X \geq 3|n=10,p=.4) = 1 - (.1209^* + .0403 + .006) = .8328$

* The individual probabilities are obtained from table E.7.

c) $P(X<2|n=10,p=.4) = P(X \leq 1|n=10,p=.4)$

$\quad P(X \leq 1|n=10,p=.4) = P(X=1) + P(X=0)$

$\quad P(X \leq 1|n=10,p=.4) = .0403 + .006 = .0463$

d) $P(X \leq 8|n=10,p=.4) = P(X=8) + P(X=7) + ... + P(X=0) = .9983$

$\qquad$ or

let Y = number of workers not working for a manufacturing firm

$\quad P(Y \geq 2|n=10,p=.6) = 1-P(Y \leq 1) = 1 - [P(Y=1) + P(Y=0)]$

$\qquad\qquad 1-P(Y \leq 1) = 1 - (.0016 + .0001) = .9983$

3. a) $\lambda = 8$ errors/4 pages

$$P(X=7 \mid \lambda=8) = \frac{e^{-8} \; 8^7}{7!} \approx .139587$$

b) $\lambda = 6$ errors/3 pages

$\quad P(X \geq 4|\lambda=6) = 1-P(X \leq 3|\lambda=6) = 1-[P(X=3)+P(X=2)+P(X=1)+P(X=0)]$

$\quad P(X \geq 4|\lambda=6) = 1 - (.0892 + .0446 + .0149 + .0025) = .8488$

4. a)

$$P(X=1 \mid n=8,p=.05) = \binom{8}{1}(.05)^1(1-.05)^7 = \frac{8!}{1! \; 7!}(.05)(.69834)$$

$P(X=1) \approx .27933$

b) $\mu_X = E[X] = n.p = (8)(.05) = .4$ defectives

c) $P(X \geq 2|n=20, p=.05) = 1-P(X \leq 1) = 1-[P(X=1)+P(X=0)]$

$$\sigma_x = \sqrt{n\ p\ (1-p)} = \sqrt{(8)\ (.05)\ (.95)} \approx .61644$$

$$P(X \geq 2 \mid n=20,\ p.05) = 1 - P(X \leq 1) = 1 - (.3774 + .3585) = .2641$$

5.

X	P(X)	(X).P(X)
10	.10	1.0
20	.30	6.0
30	.40	12.0
40	.20	8.0
total		27

$$\mu_x = 27$$

b)

X	P(X)	$X - \mu_x$	$(X - \mu_x)^2$	$(X - \mu_x)^2\ P(X)$
10	.10	-17	289	28.9
20	.30	-7	49	14.7
30	.40	3	9	3.6
40	.20	13	169	33.9
total				81

$\sigma^2_x = 81$ and $\qquad \sigma_x = 9$

6.

a) uniform distribution (each outcome is equally likely to occur)

b) P(X) = 1/26

7.

a) We need to verify that P(X=x):

X	P(X)
1	1/15
2	2/15
3	3/15
4	4/15
5	5/15

Since ΣP(X) = (1/15)+(2/15)+(3/15)+(4/15)+(5/15) = 1 and all individual probabilities are between 0 and 1, this is a probability function.

b) P(X=2) = 2/15

c) P(1 ≤ X ≤ 3) = P(X=1)+P(X=2)+P(X=3) = (1/15)+(2/15)+(3/15) = .40

d) P(X ≥ 3) = P(X=3)+P(X=4)+P(X=5) = (3/15)+(4/15)+(5/15) = .80

e)

X	P(X)	(X).P(X)
1	1/15	1/15
2	2/15	4/15
3	3/15	9/15
4	4/15	16/15
5	5/15	25/15
total		55/15

μ_X = E[X] = 55/15 = 3.6667

f)

X	P(X)	$X - \mu_x$	$(X - \mu_x)^2$	$(X - \mu_x)^2 P(X)$
1	1/15	-40/15	7.111	.4741
2	2/15	-25/15	2.777	.3704
3	3/15	-10/15	.444	.0888
4	4/15	5/15	.111	.02963
5	5/15	20/15	1.777	.5926
total				1.5553

$\sigma^2_X = 1.5553$ and $\sigma_X = 1.2472$ (std dev of the changeover time)

8.

a)

X	P(X)	X P(X)
0	.05	0
1	.10	.10
2	.10	.20
3	.15	.45
4	.20	.80
5	.25	1.25
6	.15	.90
totals	1.0	3.70

$\mu_x = \sum X P(X) = 3.70$ magazines.

b)

X	P(X)	$X - \mu_x$	$(X - \mu_x)^2$	$(X - \mu_x)^2 P(X)$
0	.05	-3.7	13.69	.6845
1	.10	-2.7	7.29	.729
2	.10	-1.7	2.89	.289
3	.15	-.7	.49	.0735
4	.20	.3	.09	.018
5	.25	1.3	1.69	.4225
6	.15	2.3	5.29	.7935
total				3.01

$\sigma^2_X = 3.01$ and $\sigma_X = \sqrt{3.01} = 1.7349$.

c)

X_i	$P(X_i)$	V_i (\$)	$V_i P(X_i)$
0	.05	-2.4	-.12
1	.10	-1.5	-.15
2	.10	-.60	-.06
3	.15	.30	.045
4	.20	1.20	.24
5	.25	2.10	.525
6	.15	3.00	.45
total	1.0		.93

$EMG = \sum_{i=1}^{n} V_i \, P(X_i) = .93$ If 6 magazines are purchased the store owner expects to make 93 cents of average profit per week.

9. a)

$$P(X=x \mid n,p) \approx \frac{e^{-(np)} \ (np)^x}{x!}$$

$$P(X=7 \mid n=1000, p=.01) \approx \frac{2.7183^{-(1000)(.01)} \ (1000)(.01)^7}{7!}$$

$$P(X=7 \mid n=1000, p=.01) \approx \frac{454}{7!} \approx .0901$$

Note that the same probability (.0901) can be directly obtained from table E.6.

b) P(X ≤ 5 | n=1000, p=.01) = P(X=0) + P(X=1) + P(X=2) +...+ P(X=5)

From table E.6., using λ = (n)(p) = (1000)(.01) = 10

P(X ≤ 5 | n=1000, p=.01) = 0 + .0005 + .0023 + .0076 + .0378

P(X ≤ 5 | n=1000, p=.01) = .0671.

c) P(X > 12) = P(X ≥ 13) = 1 - P(X ≤ 12)

P(X ≥ 13) = 1 - [P(X=12) + P(X=11) + P(X=10) +....+ P(X=0)

From table E.6. using λ = 10

P(X ≥ 13) = 1 - (.0948 + .1137 + .1251 +...+ 0)

P(X ≥ 13) = 1 - .7916 = .2084.

CHAPTER 8

The Normal Distribution

CHAPTER SUMMARY

While several discrete distributions are discussed in Chapter 7, only one continuous distribution is the topic of this chapter, the normal distribution. The normal distribution is vital to the understanding and application of statistics for three reasons. In its own right, the normal distribution can be seen in or can approximate many naturally occurring, continuous phenomena. Examples might be the height of males living in the United States, the temperature of the human body or the lifespan of goldfish. In addition, the normal distribution can, in certain instances, approximate many discrete distributions. As the discrete models can be computationally difficult, it is more efficient to use the normal approximation. Possibly the most important aspect of the normal distribution is that sampling theory (Chapter 9) is based upon the normal distribution. The concepts developed in this chapter lay the foundation for much of the material covered in the remainder of the text.

This chapter discusses the properties and assumptions of the normal distribution, the standardized normal distribution, use of probability tables and the normal approximations to the binomial Poisson distributions.

KEY CONCEPTS AND TERMS

continuous probability density functions: arising due to some measuring process on various phenomena of interest. (p. 274)

Gaussian or normal distribution: a bell-shaped, symmetrical curve ranging from negative infinity to positive infinity. Its measures of central tendency (mean, median, mode, midrange and midhinge) are all identical and its interquartile range is 1.33 standard deviations. The Gaussian curve is named after Carl Friedrich Gauss (1777-1855). (p. 275)

normal probability density function: (p. 277)

$$f(x) = \frac{1}{\sqrt{2\pi}\sigma_x} e^{-(1/2)[(x-\mu_x)/\sigma_x]^2}$$

where: e = the mathematical constant approximated by 2.71828

π = the mathematical constant approximated by 3.14159

μ_x = the population mean

σ_X = the population standard deviation

X = any value of the continuous random variable

where $-\infty < X < +\infty$

transformation formula: used to transform any normal variable to a standardized normal variable in order to determine its desired probabilities from a table of the standardized normal distribution. (p. 278)

$$Z = \frac{x-\mu_x}{\sigma_x}$$

where: Z = a standardized normal variable

μ_x = the population mean

σ_X = the population standard deviation

X = any value of the continuous random variable where $-\infty < X < +\infty$

standardized normal distribution: random variable Z always has a mean $\mu_z = 0$ and a standard deviation $\sigma_z = 1$. (p. 278)

normal probability plot: a two-dimensional plot of the observed data values on the vertical axis with their corresponding quantile values from a standardized normal distribution on the horizontal axis. (p. 296)

inverse normal scores transformation: the process of obtaining quantile values from a standard normal distribution. (p. 297)

the ith standard normal quantile, q_{zi}: the value on a standard normal distribution below which $i/(n+1)$ of the area under the curve is contained. (p. 297)

the nth (and largest) standard normal quantile, q_{zn}: the value on a standard normal distribution below which $n/(n+1)$ of the area under the curve is contained. (p. 297)

correction for continuity adjustment: requires the adding or subtracting of 0.5 from the value or values of the discrete random variable X to obtain more accurate approximations of probabilities. (p. 305)

transformation formula for a normal approximation to the binomial distribution: used to find approximate probabilities corresponding to the values of the discrete random variable X (binomially distributed) when $np \geq 5$ and $n(1-p) \geq 5$. (p. 306)

$$Z = \frac{x_a - np}{\sqrt{np(1-p)}}$$

where: Z = a standardized normal variable

μ_x = np, mean of the binomial distribution

$\sigma_X = \sqrt{np(1-p)}$, standard deviation of the binomial distribution x_a = adjusted number of successes, x, for the discrete random variable X, such that

x_a = x - .5 or x_a = x + .5 as needed

transformation formula for a normal approximation to the Poisson distribution: used to find approximate probabilities corresponding to the values of the discrete random variable X (Poisson distributed) when $\lambda \geq 5$. (p. 308)

$$Z = \frac{x_a - \lambda}{\sqrt{\lambda}}$$

where: Z = a standardized normal variable

$\mu_x = \lambda$, mean of the Poisson distribution

$\sigma_X = \sqrt{\lambda}$, standard deviation of the Poisson distribution

x_a = adjusted number of successes, x, for the discrete random variable X, such that

x_a = x - .5 or x_a = x + .5 as needed

104

REVIEW QUESTIONS

1. Although the normal distribution ranges from negative infinity to positive infinity, why is six standard deviations often used as a practical approximation of the range for normally distributed data?

2. What two descriptive, "exploratory" approaches can be taken to evaluate the "goodness-of-fit" of any particular batch of data to the normal distribution?

3. When and why would you use the correction for continuity adjustment?

4. When will the effect of the correction for continuity adjustment be negligible?

5. When using the normal approximation of the binomial or Poisson distributions, why is it important for np and n(1-p) or λ to be at least 5?

6. Explain the theory behind the normal probability plot. In other words, how are the results interpreted?

7. How does standardizing the data affect the equation for the normal distribution?

$$f(x) = \frac{1}{\sqrt{2\pi}\sigma_x} e^{-(1/2)\left[(x-\mu_x)/\sigma_x\right]^2}$$

8. Why is the concept of standardization so important to the development of the standardized normal distribution table?

9. Explain the importance of the normal distribution.

MULTIPLE CHOICE AND FILL IN QUESTIONS

1. For a continuous distribution, the exact probability of a particular value is _____ .

a) less than one.   b) more than one.

c) zero.   d) one.

e) can be determined from standardized normal distribution table

2. A standard normal distribution has a mean of _____ and a standard deviation of _____ .

3. The total area under the curve of a normal distribution is equal to _____ .

4. For a continuous distribution, $p(X < 75) = p(X \le 75)$.

a) true   b) false

5. All continuous random variables are normally distributed.

a) true   b) false

6. Which is not a property of the normal distribution?

a) identical measures of central tendency

b) interquartile range equal to 1.33 standard deviations

c) random variable is continuous and ranges from negative infinity to positive infinity

d) bell shaped and symmetrical in appearance

e) the standard deviation equals one-third the range

7. If $Z = 2$, $X = 7$ and $\mu_x = 5$, find the value of σ_x.

a) +1   b) -1   c) 0   d) +1.5   e) -1.5

EXERCISES

1. A local ice cream shop weighs their ice cream cones to make certain the cones are filled correctly. The weight of the filled cones is normally distributed with a mean of 4 ounces and a variance of .25 "squared ounces".

a) What is the probability that a cone will weigh more than 5.5 ounces?

b) What is the probability that a cone will weigh less than 3.5 ounces?

c) What is the interquartile range for this distribution? Verify your answer by using quartiles.

d) Assume σ_X = 0.5 ounces. What should the mean weight be if the owner wants no more than five percent of the cones to weigh more than 5 ounces?

2.

a) The probability that a male will be color blind is about .08. What is the probability that 3 of the 70 male students in an introductory statistics class will be color blind?

b) What is the approximate probability that 3 or fewer of the 70 male students will be color blind?

3.

a) An appliance manufacturer estimates that the scratches on refrigerators delivered to retailers is Poisson distributed with a mean of .5. What is the probability that of the next ten refrigerators which arrive there will be a total of 7 scratches?

b) What is the approximate probability that of the next 10 delivered refrigerators there will be no more than a total of 7 scratches?

4. The following data are thought to be approximately normally distributed. Test this assumption by comparing the characteristics of the data set to the properties of the normal distribution. Construct a normal probability plot to support your analysis.

71   76   69   71   67   74   68   72   71   71

110

ANSWERS TO REVIEW QUESTIONS

1. The probability of a randomly selected value of x being more than three standard deviations above or below the mean is only .0027. Approximating the range as six standard deviations will include most of the data.

2. To evaluate "goodness-of-fit", compare the characteristics of the data set with the underlying properties of the normal distribution and construct a normal probability plot.

3. When using the normal distribution to approximate discrete distributions (binomial or Poisson), the correction for continuity adjustment provides more accurate approximations of the probabilities. For a continuous distribution, the probability of obtaining a particular value is zero. To approximate the probability of a specific value of the discrete distribution using a normal approximation, the correction must be used.

4. Except when determining the probability of a specific value of a discrete distribution, the effects of the correction for continuity adjustment become negligible with larger sample sizes.

5. In order to use the normal approximation, the original distribution must be symmetric. The binomial distribution is symmetric when p = .5 or when the sample size n is large. A rule of thumb is that when np and n(1-p) are at least 5, a symmetric shape can be assumed. The Poisson distribution is similar in that as λ increases, the distribution becomes more symmetric and when λ is at least 5, again, we can assume a symmetric distribution.

6. If a data batch is normally distributed, the ordered array of observed values should be highly correlated with the standard normal quantile values calculated from the inverse normal scores transformation. The normal probability plot graphs the observed data values on the vertical axis and the quantile values on the horizontal axis. If the plotted points seem to lie either on or close to an imaginary straight line rising from the origin to the upper right corner of the graph, the normal distribution is supported.

7. Standardizing the data transforms any normal random variable X to a standardized normal random variable Z. The standardized random variable Z has a mean of zero and a standard deviation of one. The equation of a standardized normal variable is as follows:

$$f(z) = \frac{1}{\sqrt{2\pi}} e^{-(1/2)z^2}$$

8. A normal distribution is determined by its two, independent parameters μ_x and σ_X. Without standardizing the data, an infinite number of probability tables would be required. By transforming normal variables into standard normal variables, only one table is required to determine probabilities.

9. Many continuous data sets are normally distributed or can be approximated by a normal distribution. Certain discrete distributions can also be approximated by the normal distribution. The normal distribution also provides the basis for classical statistical inference.

ANSWERS TO MULTIPLE CHOICE AND FILL IN

1. c

2. zero, one

3. one

4. a

5. b

6. e (the standard deviation equals approximately 1/6 the range)

7. a

$$Z = \frac{X - \mu_x}{\sigma_x} \qquad can\ be\ rewritten\ as\ \sigma_x = \frac{X - \mu_x}{Z}$$

(solving for $\sigma_X = (7 - 5)/2 = 1 \quad \sigma_X = 1$)

SOLUTIONS TO EXERCISES

1.

a) To determine the probability, first convert the variance to a standard deviation.

$$\sigma_x = \sqrt{\sigma_x^2} = \sqrt{.25} = .50$$

Using the transformation formula, solve for Z.

$$Z = \frac{X - \mu_x}{\sigma_x} = \frac{5.5 - 4}{.5} = 3$$

This can be interpreted as: $P(X > 5.5) = P(Z > 3)$. According to the standard normal table, $P(Z > 3) = .5 - .49865 = .00135$

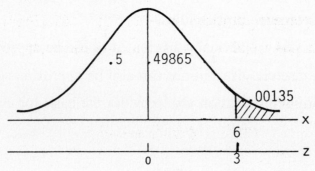

b) Using the transformation formula, again solve for Z.

$$Z = \frac{X - \mu_x}{\sigma_x} = \frac{3.5 - 4}{.5} = -1$$

This can be interpreted as: $P(X < 3.5) = P(Z < -1)$. According to the standard normal table, $P(Z < -1) = .5 - .3413 = .1587$

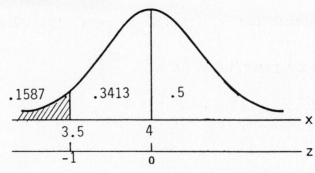

c) The interquartile range is equal to 1.33 standard deviations.

$(1.33)(.5) = .665 \approx .67$

To verify this, find the values of the first and third quartile and subtract Q_1 from Q_3. Q_1 represents 25% of the data in the left tail of the distribution which has a corresponding Z value of -.67. Q_3 represents 75% of the area of the curve with a Z value of +.67.

$$Q_1 = X = {}_x + Z\sigma_x$$
$$= 4 + -.67(.5) = 3.665$$
$$Q_3 = X = {}_x + Z\sigma_x$$
$$= 4 + .67(.5) = 4.335$$
$$Q_3 - Q_1 = 4.335 - 3.665 = .67$$

d) "No more than five percent" translates to $P\{Z > ?\} = .05$. From the standard normal table, the Z value is 1.64. $P\{Z > 1.64\} = .05$ (where .5 -.45 = .05)

$$Z = \frac{X - \mu_x}{\sigma_x} \rightarrow \mu_x = X - Z\sigma_x$$

$$= 5 - (1.64)(.5) = 4.18$$

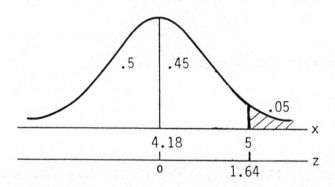

2.

a) This is a binomial distribution problem and can be solved using the binomial formula.

$$P(X=x|n,p) = \frac{n!}{x!\,(n-x)!}p^x(1-p)^{n-x}$$

$$= \frac{70!}{3!\,67!}(.08)^3(.92)^{67}$$

$$= .1050$$

Note that Table E.7 shows binomial probabilities up to $n=20$. A good hand calculator is needed to get this result.

b) Because np ≥ 5 and n(1-p) ≥ 5, a normal approximation can be used to determine the approximate probability.

$$Z = \frac{x_a - np}{\sqrt{np(1-p)}}$$

$$= \frac{3.5 - 5.6}{\sqrt{(5.6)(.92)}}$$

$$= -.925$$

P(Z ≤ -.93) = .5 - .3238 = .1762. Note that the exact binomial probability of finding 3 or fewer color blind males out of 70 is .1790.

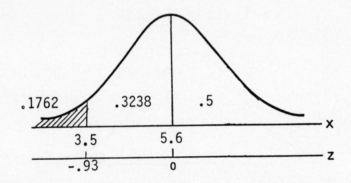

3.

a) Using the Poisson table, λ = (.5) (10) = 5, X = 7 P(X = 7| λ = 5) = .1044

b) To compute the probability of 7 or less, it is easier to use a normal approximation to the Poisson distribution.

$$Z = \frac{x_a - \lambda}{\sqrt{\lambda}} = \frac{7.5 - 5}{\sqrt{5}} = 1.118$$

P(Z ≤ 1.12) = .5 + .3686 = .8686. Note that the exact Poisson probability is .8666.

4. The following summary statistics and box plot are computer generated:

```
      Cases  = 10          Mean        = 71
      Low    = 67          St. Dev. = 2.666667
      High   = 76          1st Quartile = 69
      Range  = 9           2nd Quartile = 71
      Median = 71          3rd Quartile = 72
```

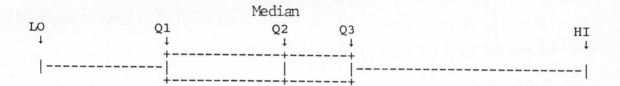

The mode, median and mean all equal 71. The midrange $\{(67 + 76)/2\}$ equals 71.5 and the midhinge $\{(Q_1 + Q_3)/2\}$ equals 70.5. These all indicate a slightly right skewed distribution that appears close to normal.

The interquartile range $(Q_3 - Q_1)$ is 3. The standard deviation times 1.33 is equal to 3.55, close to the interquartile range. Using the range (76 - 67) of 9, the standard deviation can be approximated by 9 divided by 6 which is 1.5. We should be cautious in using this approximation (the standard deviation approximately equals one-sixth the range) because it is only appropriate when the sample size is relatively large. The rule of thumb is that n must be at least 10. This approximate estimated value of the standard deviation can be compared to the actual standard deviation of 2.67.

The following table was developed using the empirical rule to compare observed and expected percentage of data.

	Actual %	Expected %
mean plus or minus one standard deviation		
$71 \pm 2.67 = 68.33$ to 73.67	60%	68%
mean plus or minus 1.28 standard deviations		
$71 \pm (2.67)(1.28) = 67.58$ to 74.42	80%	80%
mean plus or minus two standard deviations		
$71 \pm (2)(2.67) = 65.66$ to 76.34	100%	95%

116

The comparisons of expected vs. observed percentages further support the normal distribution.

The normal probability plot is constructed using the inverse normal scores transformation.

Q_1 = -1.34   (1/11 = .09 P{Z ≤ -1.34} = .09)
Q_2 = - .92
Q_3 = - .61
Q_4 = - .36
Q_5 = - .13
Q_6 =   .13
Q_7 =   .36
Q_8 =   .61
Q_9 =   .92
Q_{10} = 1.34

Normal Probability Plot

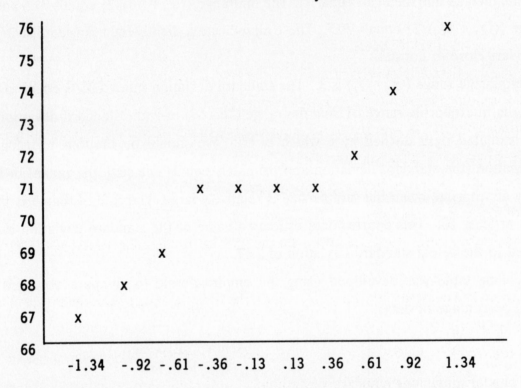

This plot also indicates slight right skewness of the data.

CHAPTER 9

Sampling Distributions

CHAPTER SUMMARY

Prior to this chapter, the textbook has concentrated on descriptive statistics as well as probability and certain probability distributions. Data from both populations and samples were charted, graphed and analyzed. Probabilities based on known population parameters were determined for various distributions.

This chapter introduces the concept of inferential statistics, the method of estimating characteristics of a population from only the sample data. The theory of the sampling distribution of the mean and the central limit theorem, both fundamental to the understanding of inferential statistics, are included in this chapter. Sampling from nonnormal, as well as, normal populations is also discussed.

KEY CONCEPTS AND TERMS

sampling distribution: a distribution made up of all possible samples of equal sample size that could have occurred from a population of interest. (p. 320)

unbiasedness: the average of all the possible sample means (of a given sample size n) will be equal to the population mean $_x$. (p. 321)

efficiency: refers to the precision of the sample statistic as an estimator of the population parameter. (p. 323)

consistency: refers to the effect of the sample size on the usefulness of the estimator. (p. 323)

law of large numbers: the variance of the sample mean approaches zero as n approaches infinity. (p. 323)

standard error of the mean: the measure of the variability of the sample mean from sample to sample. The standard error is the value of the standard deviation of the sample mean. (p. 324) $\sigma_{\bar{x}} = \dfrac{\sigma_x}{\sqrt{n}}$ and when sampling without replacement from a finite population. $\sigma_{\bar{x}} = \dfrac{\sigma_x}{\sqrt{n}} \cdot \sqrt{\dfrac{N-n}{N-1}}$

The Z transformation formula is $Z = \dfrac{\bar{X}-\mu_{\bar{x}}}{\sigma_{\bar{x}}} = \dfrac{\bar{X}-\mu_x}{\dfrac{\sigma_x}{\sqrt{n}}}$

central limit theorem: As the sample size (number of observations in each sample) gets "large enough", the sampling distribution of the mean can be approximated by the normal distribution. This is true regardless of the shape of the distribution of the individual values in the population. (p. 329)

sampling distribution of the proportion: a distribution made up of all possible samples of equal sample size that could have occurred from a population of interest when the random variable is qualitative. (p. 334)

The proportion is calculated as $p_s = \dfrac{X}{n} = \dfrac{number\ of\ successes}{sample\ size}$

The Z transformation formula is $Z = \dfrac{p_s-p}{\sqrt{\dfrac{p(1-p)}{n}}}$

where p_s = sample proportion
       p = population proportion

$\sigma_{p_s} = \sqrt{\dfrac{p(1-p)}{n}}$

and when sampling without replacement from a finite population.

$\sigma_{p_s} = \sqrt{\dfrac{p(1-p)}{n}} \cdot \sqrt{\dfrac{N-n}{N-1}}$

REVIEW QUESTIONS

1. The finite population correction factor has what affect on the standard error of the mean and the standard error of the proportion?

2. Why is the arithmetic mean the most widely used measure of central tendency?

3. What are the practical implications of the central limit theorem?

4. What sample size is considered "large enough" for the central limit theorem to justify a normal approximation?

5. What is the required sample size for the sampling distribution to be a normal when sampling with replacement from a normal population?

6. Explain why the standard error of the mean is less than the standard deviation of the original population for n > 1.

MULTIPLE CHOICE AND FILL IN QUESTIONS

1. A sample mean is to the _____ _____ as an individual observation is to the population.

2. _____ is a property of the mean which states that as the sample size gets larger, the more likely it is that the estimator will be close to the parameter.

3. If the average of all sample means ($\mu_{\bar{x}}$) is equal to the population mean ($_x$), the measure is considered to be _____.

4. An estimator is considered _____ if it comes closer to estimating the parameter than any other estimator.

5. If the sample size (n) is quadrupled, the standard error of the mean
a) doubles.   b) quadruples.
c) decreases by half.   d) decreases by four times.
e) stays the same.

6. The chance that the mean of a sample of 25 will be "close to" the population mean is greater than the chance that a single individual value will be.
a) true   b) false

7. The sampling distribution of the mean is based on a population of _____ random variables, whereas the sampling distribution of the proportion is based on a population of _____ random variables.

8. If a population is not normal, the sampling distribution of the means from that population will approach a _____ distribution as the sample size _____.

EXERCISES

1.

a) The scheduled route for a particular railroad from City A to City B is 1387 miles and averages 46.33 hours from origin to destination. The distribution of transit hours is normally distributed with a standard deviation of 2.5 hours. What is the probability that the average transit time for the next nine days will be greater than 48 hours?

b) What is the probability that the average transit time will be between 45 and 47 hours for the next nine days?

c) If the dispatcher wants to be 90% certain that the average transit time for the next nine days will be on time, what should she consider "on time"?

2. The quality control manager has determined that 6% of all orders require rework. If 1250 orders went out this week, what is the probability that more than 100 required rework?

3. A 200 unit batch of a particular plastic item has just arrived. The average tensile strength for the population is 48 pounds per square inch with a standard deviation of 4 pounds. A sample of size 36 is tested. What is the probability that the sample mean is less than 46.8?

ANSWERS TO REVIEW QUESTIONS

1. The finite population correction factor will always be less than or equal to one because the numerator is always less than or equal to the denominator. The result will be a decrease in the standard error (or remain the same if $n = 1$).

2. The arithmetic mean is unbiased, efficient and consistent. Because the mean possesses all of these properties, it is widely used and often the best measure.

3. Due to the central limit theorem, it is not necessary to know the distribution of the population from which you are sampling. If the sample size is "large enough" it is correct

to approximate the sampling distribution with a normal distribution.

4. The size of the sample is dependent upon the symmetry and shape of the population of interest. As a general rule, n = 30 is sufficient for a normal approximation. Often, however, a sample size of less will allow for a normal approximation, particularly if some knowledge of the population is available.

5. The sampling distribution from a normal population when sampling with replacement will always be normal for any size n.

6. The standard deviation of the population represents all individual observations including the high and low extremes. The standard error of the mean includes only averages of individual values so that the extreme highs and lows are "averaged out".

ANSWERS TO MULTIPLE CHOICE AND FILL IN

1. sampling distribution

2. consistency

3. unbiased

4. efficient

5. c

6. a

7. quantitative, qualitative

8. normal, increases

SOLUTIONS TO EXERCISES

1.

a) Because the population is known to be normal, the sampling distribution can be approximated with a normal distribution.

$$Z = \frac{\overline{X} - \mu_x}{\frac{\sigma_x}{\sqrt{n}}} = \frac{48 - 46.3}{\frac{2.5}{\sqrt{9}}} = 2.04$$

$P(X > 48) = P(Z > 2.04) = .5 - .4793 = .0207$

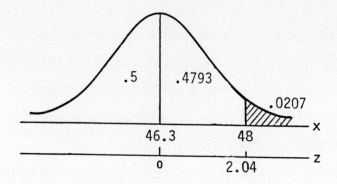

b)

$$Z = \frac{\overline{X} - \mu_x}{\frac{\sigma_x}{\sqrt{n}}} = \frac{45 - 46.3}{\frac{2.5}{\sqrt{9}}} = -1.56$$

$$Z = \frac{\overline{X} - \mu_x}{\frac{\sigma_x}{\sqrt{n}}} = \frac{47 - 46.3}{\frac{2.5}{\sqrt{9}}} = .84$$

$$P(45 < \overline{X} < 47) = P(-1.56 < Z < .84) = .4406 + .2995 = .7401$$

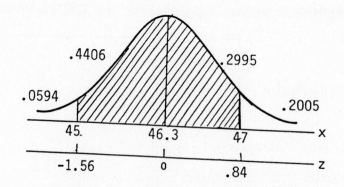

c) $P(Z < 1.28) = .90$

$$\overline{X} = \mu_x + Z\frac{\sigma_x}{\sqrt{n}} = 46.3 + (1.28)\frac{2.5}{\sqrt{9}} = 47.37$$

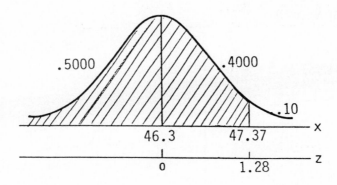

2.

$$p_s = \frac{100}{1250} = .08 \text{ and } n = 1250$$

$$Z = \frac{p_s - p}{\frac{\sqrt{p(1-p)}}{n}} = \frac{.08 - .06}{\sqrt{\frac{(.06)(.94)}{1250}}} = 2.98$$

$P(p_s > .08) = P(Z > 2.98) = .5 - .4986 = .0014$

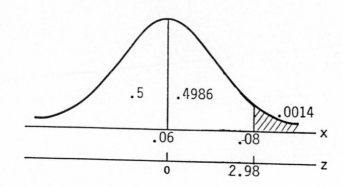

126

3. This exercise illustrates sampling from a finite population

(N = 200) and requires use of the finite population correction factor.

$$Z = \frac{\overline{X} - \mu_x}{\dfrac{\sigma_x}{\sqrt{n}}\sqrt{\dfrac{N-n}{N-1}}} = \frac{46.8 - 48}{\dfrac{4}{\sqrt{36}}\sqrt{\dfrac{200-36}{200-1}}} = -1.98$$

$P(\overline{X} < 46.8) = P(Z < -1.98) = .5 - .4761 = .0239$

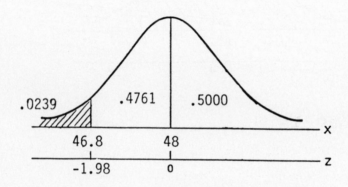

CHAPTER 10

Estimation

CHAPTER SUMMARY

The coverage of the topics in the earlier chapters, including descriptive statistics, probability, probability distributions and sampling distributions set the foundation for making inferences about a population based on the sample data. In chapter three, we computed a sample mean and a sample variance to describe and summarize sample data. Any conclusions we reached related only to the sample data set. In this chapter, various descriptive measures such as a mean and a variance are calculated with a different objective. Now, our interest has shifted to what these sample measures can tell us about the population from which the sample data is selected.

KEY CONCEPTS AND TERMS

statistical inference: the process of using sample results to draw conclusions about the characteristics of a population. (p. 328)

point estimate: a single sample statistic that is used to estimate the true population parameter. (p. 328)

interval estimate: a range of data constructed from the point estimate by using the appropriate sampling distribution so that we have a specified confidence or probability of correctly estimating the true value of the population parameter. (p. 328)

$(1 - \alpha)$ confidence interval: $(1 - \alpha)$ is the likelihood that the interval includes the true population parameter. (p. 330)

critical value: value of the test statistic obtained from a specified distribution to construct a confidence interval. (p. 331)

(1 - α)% confidence interval for the population mean (μ) with σ_X known:

$$\overline{X} \pm Z \frac{\sigma_x}{\sqrt{n}}$$

where $\overline{X}$ = sample mean

σ_x = population standard deviation

n = sample size

Z = critical value of the standardized normal distribution corresponding to an area of $(1-\alpha)/2$ from the center of the distribution in the upper tail.

degrees of freedom: the number of variables to which values may be freely assigned until all values for the remaining variables are determined by the restrictions. In the computation of the sample variance (s^2), $\overline{X}$ imposes the single restriction. If there are five observations, four of them may assume any value but after the first four observations have been assigned the value of the fifth observation is automatically determined by the restriction, giving us (n-1 = 4) degrees of freedom. (p. 335)

student's t distribution: if the random variable X is normally distributed, then the statistic $\dfrac{\overline{X} - \mu_x}{\dfrac{s_x}{\sqrt{n}}}$ has a t distribution with n-1 degrees of freedom. (p. 334)

properties of the student's t distribution: (p. 334)

a) similar to standard normal (z) distribution such that it is bell shaped and symmetric;

b) it has more area in the tails and less in the center than the normal distribution;

c) as the number of degrees of freedom increases the t distribution gradually approaches the z distribution.

$(1 - \alpha)$% confidence interval for the population mean (μ) with σ_X unknown: (p. 336)

$$\overline{X} \pm t_{n-1} \frac{s}{\sqrt{n}}$$

where $\overline{X}$ = sample mean

s = sample standard deviation

n = sample size

t_{n-1} = critical value of the t distribution with n-1 degrees of freedom for an area of $\alpha/2$ in the upper tail.

bootstrapping estimation procedure: involves taking an initial sample from a population frame, and then repeated sampling from the initial sample to form a confidence interval for the population mean, μ_x. (p. 356)

steps in bootstrapping estimation procedure:

1. Draw a random sample of size n without replacement from population of size N.

2. Resample the initial sample by selecting n observations with replacement from the n observations in the initial sample.

3. Compute $\overline{X}$ from this resample.

4. Repeat steps 2 and 3 m times, where $100 < m < 1000$.

5. Form the resampling distribution of the means by ordering the resample means from smallest to largest.

6. Form the $(1 - \alpha)*100$ bootstrap confidence interval of the population mean μ_x by determining the $(\alpha/2)*100$ percentile mean in the ordered array and $(1 - \alpha/2)*100$ percentile mean in the ordered array.

purpose of using bootstrap confidence interval instead of the traditional confidence interval: bootstrap interval has less stringent assumptions (i.e. the underlying population does not have to be approximately normally distributed) (p. 356)

(1 - α)% confidence interval for a future individual value: (p. 339)

$$\overline{X} \pm t_{n-1} s \sqrt{1 + \frac{1}{n}}$$

(1 - α)% confidence interval for the population proportion: (p. 341)

$$p_s \pm Z \sqrt{\frac{p_s(1 - p_s)}{n}}$$

where Z = the critical value of the standard normal distribution.

p_s = sample proportion (X/n);

X = number of observations selected;

n = total number of observations in the sample.

sampling error for a mean: the difference between a sample estimate and true value of the population parameter being estimated. (p. 344)

Sampling error is calculated with the following formula:

$$e = \frac{Z \, \sigma_X}{\sqrt{n}}$$

sample size (n) for a mean: solving the sampling error equation for n, the following sample size equation is obtained: (p. 344)

$$n = \frac{Z^2 \, \sigma_X^2}{e^2}$$

pilot study: uses a small sample (usually 20 to 30 observations) to gain some information about the population and to generate initial estimates of the population parameters, if historical data is not available. (p. 345)

sampling error for a proportion: the difference between the average sample proportion (p_s) and the average population proportion (p). (pp. 346 -347)

The formula for sampling error for a proportion is:

sample size for a proportion: determined by solving the sampling error for a proportion formula for n. (p. 347)

$$e = Z\sqrt{\frac{p(1-p)}{n}}$$

$$sample\ size = n = \frac{Z^2p(1-p)}{e^2}$$

finite population correction (fpc) factor: It is used to reduce the standard error by the factor given below if sampling without replacement from small finite populations. (p. 348)

$$fpc\ factor = \sqrt{\frac{N-n}{N-1}}$$

All of the sample size and the interval estimate formulas for the mean and the proportion given above need to be multiplied by the finite population correction factor when sampling from finite populations without replacement.

REVIEW QUESTIONS

1. Why is it beneficial to use the interval estimate over the point estimate?

2. When is it necessary to use the finite population correction factor in the determination of the sample size?

3. What is the difference between sampling error for the population mean and standard error of the mean?

4. In estimating the interval for the population mean, under what condition(s) is it appropriate to use the student's t distribution in lieu of the standard normal distribution?

5. What factors affect the sample size?

6. List the factors affecting the width of a confidence interval for the population mean?

7. List three possible ways of obtaining an estimate of the population standard deviation.

8. What is the purpose of using bootstrapping estimation procedure rather than a traditional confidence interval procedure?

9. What is the primary **disadvantage** of developing a bootstrap confidence interval instead of a traditional confidence interval using t distribution.

MULTIPLE CHOICE AND FILL IN QUESTIONS

1. The student's t distribution approaches the standard normal distribution as

a) the sample size decreases.

b) the degrees of freedom increases.

c) the sampling error increases.

d) the standard error decreases.

e) the standard deviation increases.

2. The width of the confidence interval decreases as:

a) 1-α increases.

b) the population standard deviation increases.

c) the sample size increases.

d) the sample mean increases.

3. If the distribution of a variable is normal and the population standard deviation is known, the standard normal distribution is used to calculate a confidence interval for the population mean regardless of the size of the sample.

a) true   b) false

4. The smaller the permitted sampling error the smaller the sample size.

a) true   b) false

5. As confidence level (1-α) increases, the width of the confidence interval

a) decreases.   b) does not change.   c) increases.

6. In calculating the width of the confidence interval for the mean of an infinite population, which one of the following factors is not needed?

a) the standard deviation

b) the confidence level

c) the number of observations in the sample

d) the number of observations in the population

7. Point estimates are usually not equal to the population parameters.

a) true   b) false

8. If a Z statistic is inadvertently used in place of a t statistic with a small sample size, the length of the confidence interval is

a) understated.   b) not affected.   c) overstated.

9. In order to develop a bootstrap confidence interval the minimum number of samples to be taken is approximately _____.

a) 10   b) 30   c) 100   d) 1000   e) 10,000

10. In developing a bootstrap confidence interval, resampling is done from

a) the population.   b) the initial sample.

11. In developing a bootstrap confidence interval, after obtaining the initial sample from the population, the remaining sampling is done

a) with replacement.   b) without replacement.

136

EXERCISES

1. A taste test of various popular soft drinks was conducted. In a random sample of 400 prospective customers 80 of them preferred "Cola of the Sea" to all other brands of soft drinks. Determine a 93% confidence interval for the true proportion of all prospective customers preferring "Cola of the Sea". Write one sentence explaining the meaning of your interval.

2. A fastener manufacturer wants to determine the average torque value for a certain product (locknut). How many locknuts should the company sample if it wishes to be 94% confident of being within 3 foot-pounds of the true average? Assume that the variance is 144.

3. The XYL company performs incoming inspection of the goods from a plastics supplier. A 120 unit batch of a particular plastic item has just arrived. Determine a 99% confidence interval for the true population mean tensile strength of this batch if a randomly selected 16 units from the batch has a sample mean of 46.8 pounds per square inch and a sample standard deviation of pounds per square inch. Write a sentence explaining your interval.

4. Schmidt and Sell Inc., a newly formed public accounting company, wants to determine the average revenue per job for their company. The company has completed work and gotten paid on a total of 100 jobs. What size sample should they take if they want to be 85% confident of being within $100 of the true mean population revenue per job for their company. Assume that the previous survey of another similar company indicated a standard deviation of $600.

5. Monson and Malkowski Inc., a construction company, wants to determine the proportion of the time the vendors deliver the material shipments late in the home building industry. What size of sample (number of deliveries) should they take from the industry, if they want to be 97% confident of being within 2.2% of the true population proportion of the late deliveries.

ANSWERS TO REVIEW QUESTIONS

1. The probability that the point estimate will exactly equal the parameter being estimated is zero. Therefore, the interval estimate provides the user with a probability $(1-\alpha)$ of being within a given number of standard deviations around the true population parameter. This allows the decision-maker to estimate not only a single number, but also the possible error with respect to the parameter being estimated.

2. In determining the sample size, the finite population correction factor is used when sampling from a small finite population without replacement.

3. The sampling error for the population mean is the difference between a sample mean $(\overline{X})$ and the value of the true population parameter (μ), while the standard error of the mean $(\sigma_{\overline{x}})$ is the standard deviation of the sample mean, which measures the variability of the mean among samples.

4. The t distribution is used when the population standard deviation is not known (is estimated), while the Z distribution is used when the population standard deviation is known. However, since the t distribution approaches the standard normal as the sample size increases, we can use t distribution in lieu of the standard normal distribution for large sample sizes.

5. - confidence level desired;
   - sampling error permitted;
   - the standard deviation.

6. - sample size;
   - the standard deviation;.
   - confidence level desired.

7. - historical data (if available);
   - pilot study;
   - another similar study.

8. The bootstrapping estimation procedure is used in lieu of the traditional confidence interval procedure (based on the t distribution) if the population from which the sample is selected is highly skewed (significantly departs from the assumption of normal distribution). If the assumption of normality is significantly violated, then the resulting traditional confidence interval may be erroneous. In addition, the bootstrap confidence interval should also be preferred over the traditional confidence interval when the population parameters (μ_x and σ_x) are not known and cannot accurately be estimated. In summary, the traditional confidence interval has more stringent assumptions, i.e. the population mean is known and the shape of the population can be approximated by normal distribution.

9. The bootstrapping estimation procedure is far more computationally cumbersome and more computer intensive than the traditional estimation procedure based on the t distribution.

ANSWERS TO MULTIPLE CHOICE AND FILL IN

1. b	6. d
2. c	7. a
3. a	8. a
4. b	9. c
5. c	10. b
	11. a

SOLUTIONS TO EXERCISES

1. n = 400;   p = 80/400 = .2,   1-p = 1-.2

   For a confidence level of 93%, z = 1.81.

$$confidence\ interval = .2 \pm 1.81\sqrt{\frac{(.2)(.8)}{400}}$$

confidence interval = .2 ± .0362

Therefore the 93% confidence interval ranges from .1638 to .2362. We are 93% certain that the interval from .1638 to .2362 includes the true value of the population proportion.

2. σ^2 = 144; the permitted sampling error = e = 3.

   For a 94% confidence level, z = 1.88

$$n = \frac{(1.88)^2 (144)}{3^2} \approx 57\ locknuts$$

3. N = 120 (population size);   n = 16 sample size;

   $\overline{X}$ = 46.8 pounds;   s = 4

   99% confidence level results in a t value of 2.9467.

Since the sample is taken from a small finite population without replacement, the finite population correction factor must be used.

$$confidence\ interval = 46.8 \pm 2.9467 \ \frac{4}{\sqrt{16}} \sqrt{\frac{120-16}{120-1}}$$

$$confidence\ interval = 46.8 \pm 2.755$$

The confidence interval ranges from 44.045 to 49.555.

We are 99% sure that the interval from 44.045 to 49.555 includes the true value of the average population tensile strength of this batch.

4. For an 85% confidence level, z = 1.44;

   N = 100 (population size)   e = $100 (permitted sampling error)

   $\sigma_x = \$600$

   $$n_0 = \frac{(1.44)^2 \ (600)^2}{(100)^2} = 74.6496$$

   $$n = \frac{(74.6496) \ (100)}{(74.6496) \ + \ (100-1)} \approx 43 \ observations$$

5. For a 97% confidence level, find .97/2 = .485 in the body of the standard normal table (table E.2.) and read the corresponding Z value (Z = 2.17).

   e = 2.2% . Since no estimate of the average proportion is available, p = .5 is used to obtain the most conservative estimate of the sample size.

   $$n = \frac{(2.17)^2 \ (.5) \ (.5)}{(.022)^2} \approx 2433 \ observations$$

NOTES

CHAPTER 11

Fundamentals of Hypothesis Testing

CHAPTER SUMMARY

The previous chapter discusses the use of estimation to make inferences about population parameters based only on sample data. Hypothesis testing, the topic of this chapter, is an application of inferential statistics. In hypothesis testing, mutually exclusive hypotheses are stated about the population. The sample data are then used to determine which hypothesis is more reasonable; which hypothesis does the sample data support.

Included in this chapter are two kinds of errors that can be made in rejecting or not rejecting hypotheses, the concept of power and power curves. Meta-analysis is also introduced in this chapter.

KEY CONCEPTS AND TERMS

null hypothesis, H_0: the hypothesis that is always tested. A null hypothesis is always one of status quo or no difference. The null hypothesis contains the equality. (p. 385)

alternative hypothesis, H_1: is set up as the opposite of the null hypothesis and represents the conclusion supported if the null hypothesis is rejected. The alternative hypothesis never contains the equality. (p. 385)

test statistic: measures how close the sample value has come to the null hypothesis. (p. 391)

region of rejection (critical region): consisting of the values of the test statistic that are unlikely to occur if the null hypothesis is true and more likely to occur if the null hypothesis is false. If the test statistic falls into the region of rejection, the null hypothesis is rejected. (p. 387)

region of nonrejection: consisting of the values of the test statistic that are likely to occur if the null hypothesis is true and unlikely to occur if the null hypothesis is false. If the test statistic falls into the region of nonrejection, the null hypothesis cannot be rejected. (p. 387)

critical value: divides the rejection region from the nonrejection region. (p. 387)

Type I error: occurs if the null hypothesis H_0 is rejected when in fact it is true and should not be rejected. (p. 388)

Type II error: occurs if the null hypothesis H_0 is not rejected when it is false and should be rejected. (p. 388)

α **(alpha):** probability of committing a Type I error. (p. 388)

ß **(beta):** probability of committing a Type II error. (p. 388)

level of significance: the probability of committing a Type I error (α). (p. 388)

confidence coefficient: the complement $(1 - \alpha)$ of the probability of a Type I error. When multiplied by 100 percent, this yields the confidence level. (P. 388)

power: the complement $(1 - ß)$ of the probability of a Type II error is called the power of a statistical test. Power is the probability of rejecting the null hypothesis when it is false (and should be rejected) (p. 389)

two-tailed test: rejection region is divided into the two tails of the distribution. (p. 391)

p value: is the probability of obtaining a test statistic equal to or more extreme than the result observed from the sample data, given that the null hypothesis H_0 is true. (p. 394)

one-tailed test: the entire rejection region is contained in one tail of the distribution. (p. 398)

power curve: the power of the test for various possible values of $_1$. (p. 405)

sample size based on α and ß risk: (p. 408)

$$n = \frac{\sigma_x^2 (Z_\alpha - Z_\beta)^2}{(\mu_0 - \mu_1)^2}$$

Where σ^2_x = variance in the population

Z_α = Z value for a given α level of significance

Z_β = Z value for a given ß risk of Type II error

μ_0 = value of the population mean under the null hypothesis

μ_1 = value of the population mean under the alternative hypothesis

meta-analysis: an objective and quantitative methodology used for combining and summarizing previous research endeavors on a particular subject into an overall or global finding. (p. 414)

REVIEW QUESTIONS

1. What determines the level of ß for a particular study?

2. Explain the tradeoffs between making Type I and Type II errors.

3. What is the effect of sample size on α and ß?

4. Compare a one-tailed and a two-tailed test.

5. Compare a 90% confidence interval to a two-tailed hypothesis test, $\alpha = .10$.

6. Name three methods of improving the power of the test.

7. Discuss the advantages as well as the disadvantages of meta-analysis.

MULTIPLE CHOICE AND FILL IN QUESTIONS

1. The _____ hypothesis always contains the equality.

2. If α is decreased, then β will be _____.

3. If the p value is _____ α, the null hypothesis is not rejected; if the p value is _____ α, the null hypothesis is rejected.

4. The power of the statistical test depends upon how different the true mean is from the value being hypothesized (under H_0).

a) true   b) false

5. If a hypothesis is not rejected at the .05 level of significance, it will _____ be rejected at the .01 level.

a) never   b) sometimes   c) always

6. As α (the probability of Type I error) increases, the power of the test _____.

a) decreases   b) increases

c) cannot be determined   d) remains the same

EXERCISES

1.

a) A national motor carrier purchased electronic engines to replace the older, manually controlled models. The manual engines averaged 6.5 miles per gallon (mpg) with a standard deviation of 0.9. In testing 25 trucks with the new electronic engines, the sample mean was found to be 7 mpg. Construct a 90% confidence-interval estimate of μ_x. Using this interval, has there been a change in the miles per gallon in electronic versus manual engines? After constructing the confidence interval, answer the same question using hypothesis testing. ($\alpha = .10$)

b) What is the power of the test if the true mean for electronic engines is 7 miles per gallon? ($\alpha = .10$)

c) If management suspected, prior to purchasing the engines, that mpg would increase with electronic engines, how would the power of the test be affected? What would the power of the test be under these circumstances? (Again, assume a true mean of 7 and α = .10)

d) What is the required sample size to ensure power of 95%, with all else remaining the same as in question c?

ANSWERS TO REVIEW QUESTIONS

1. The chosen level of α and the sample size will determine the level of ß.
2. For a given sample size, the decision maker must balance the two types of errors. By decreasing the probability of a Type I error, the probability of a Type II error is increased. If a Type II error is more "costly" to the decision maker, α should be increased to decrease ß. The values for α and ß depend on the importance of each risk in a particular problem.
3. Increasing the sample size will decrease ß, the probability of Type II error for a given level of α. Alpha will remain the same because it is arbitrarily chosen by the decision maker, not based on results of the study.

4. A one-tailed test places the entire rejection region in one side of the distribution while the two-tailed test divides the rejection region into both tails of the distribution. The one-tailed test is required when the alternative hypothesis focuses in a particular direction (< or >) and the two-tailed test is used when the alternative hypothesis is nondirectional (≠). All else being equal, the one-tailed test is more powerful.

5. The confidence interval and two-tailed hypothesis test are both based on the same set of concepts. The confidence interval can be used to test a null hypothesis. If the interval contains the hypothesized value, the null hypothesis cannot be rejected. If the hypothesized value is not contained within the confidence interval, the null hypothesis should be rejected.

6. Power can be increased by 1) increasing the sample size n, 2) increasing the level of significance, α, 3) using a one-tailed test instead of a two-tailed test.

7. Meta-analysis is a quantitative method of synthesizing prior research. This ability to integrate prior findings is important. However, if previous studies used different definitions, measurement scales and methodology, care must be taken in interpreting the results of the aggregated meta-analysis.

ANSWERS TO MULTIPLE CHOICE AND FILL IN

1. null

2. increased

3. greater than or equal to, less than

4. a

5. a

6. b

SOLUTIONS TO EXERCISES

1.

a) A 90% confidence interval of the hypothesized mean is first constructed.

$$\overline{X} \pm Z_{\frac{1-\alpha}{2}} \frac{\sigma_x}{\sqrt{n}} = 7 \pm (1.645) \frac{.9}{\sqrt{25}} = 7 \pm .30$$

$P(6.7 \le$ _x $\le 7.3) = .90$

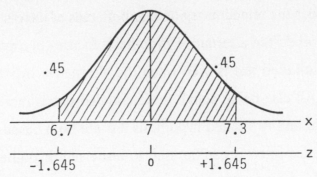

$H_0: \mu_x = 6.5$

$H_1: \mu_x \neq 6.5$

$\alpha = .10$ Critical value of $Z = 1.645$ Reject H_0 if $Z > 1.645$ or $Z < -1.645$

$$Z = \frac{\overline{X} - \mu_1}{\frac{\sigma_x}{\sqrt{n}}} = \frac{7 - 6.5}{\frac{.9}{\sqrt{25}}} = 2.77$$

Since $2.77 > 1.645$, we reject the null hypothesis (H_0). There has been a significant increase in the mpg by switching from manual engines to electronic engines.

In addition, since the confidence interval does not include the hypothesized value of 6.5, the same conclusion is reached (the null hypothesis is rejected).

b)

$$\overline{X}_u = \mu_x + Z \frac{\sigma_x}{\sqrt{n}} = 6.5 + (1.645) \frac{.9}{\sqrt{25}} = 6.8$$

$$\overline{X}_L = \mu_x + Z \frac{\sigma_x}{\sqrt{n}} = 6.5 + (-1.6455) \frac{.9}{\sqrt{25}} = 6.2$$

$$Z = \frac{\overline{X}_U - \mu_1}{\frac{\sigma_x}{\sqrt{n}}} = \frac{6.8 - 7}{\frac{.9}{\sqrt{25}}} = -1.11$$

$$Z = \frac{\overline{X}_L - \mu_1}{\frac{\sigma_x}{\sqrt{n}}} = \frac{6.2 - 7}{\frac{.9}{\sqrt{25}}} = -4.44$$

P(Z < -1.11) = .5 - .3665 = .1335

Note that the area below 6.2 is zero for the true distribution of electronic engines.

ß = .1335   Power = 1 - ß = 1 - .1335 = .8665

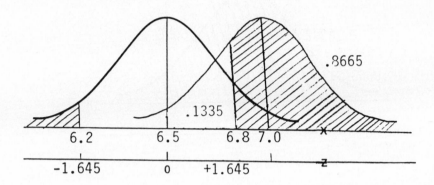

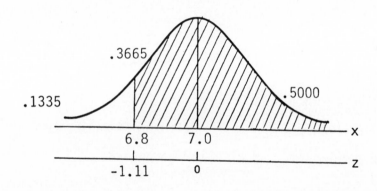

c) Knowing the direction of the alternative hypothesis allows the test to focus in one tail of the distribution which will increase the power of the test.

$$\overline{X}_u = \mu_x + Z\frac{\sigma_x}{\sqrt{n}} = 6.5 + (1.28)\frac{.9}{\sqrt{25}} = 6.73$$

$$Z = \frac{\overline{X} - \mu_1}{\frac{\sigma_x}{\sqrt{n}}} = \frac{6.73 - 7}{\frac{.9}{\sqrt{25}}} = -1.50$$

$P(Z < -1.50) = .5 - .4332 = .0668$

$\beta = .0668$ Power $= 1 - \beta = 1 - .0668 = .9332$

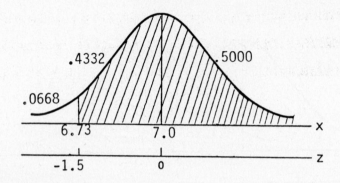

d)

$$n = \frac{\sigma_x^2(Z_\alpha - Z_\beta)^2}{(\mu_0 - \mu_1)^2} = \frac{.9^2(1.28 + 1.645)^2}{(6.5 - 7)^2} = 27.7 \approx 28$$

CHAPTER 12

One Sample Tests With Numerical Data

CHAPTER SUMMARY

The previous chapter discussed the fundamental concepts associated with hypothesis testing. In chapter 11 we made inferences about a population mean based on sample data when the standard deviation is unknown. In this chapter, we will learn other commonly used one sample tests involving numerical data. We will continue to apply the many of the fundamental concepts of inferential statistics that we have learned in the previous three chapters. This chapter covers test of hypotheses for the mean when the population standard deviation is unknown, for the median, for the variance or the standard deviation and for randomness.

In addition, the chapter demonstrates the differences between what is known as classical or **parametric** statistical methods and a set of alternative tests to classical procedures, commonly called **nonparametric methods**. The assumptions of **parametric** tests include: 1) the population from which the sample is drawn can be approximated by a normal distribution or large samples are selected to ensure that the sampling distribution approaches the normal distribution; 2) the level of measurement is at least interval so that it is possible to determine the numerical difference between two given observations.

Nonparametric procedures have less restrictive assumptions, especially with respect to the distribution of the population(s) and level of measurement. They become viable alternatives when the assumptions of the classical procedures are not met.

KEY CONCEPTS AND TERMS

parametric test procedures: require at least interval level of measurement, involve hypothesis testing of a specified parameter values and require other stringent assumptions (such as the distribution from which the sample is drawn has a normal distribution). (p. 423)

distribution free procedures: inferential methods which do not depend on restrictive assumptions about the levels of measurement and the distribution of the population(s) and other restrictive assumptions associated with the parametric procedures. (p. 423)

nonparametric procedures: inferential methods which are not concerned about the population parameters. (p. 423)

distribution free procedures are used when:

- the level of measurement is nominal (categorical data) or ordinal (rank ordered data);

- the assumptions required for the parametric counterpart method cannot be met.

nonparametric procedures are used when:

- testing features other than population parameters (such as randomness, independence, symmetry, goodness of fit).

a procedure is considered **robust** if it is relatively insenistive to slight violations in the assumptions and the true level of significance (α) and the power of the test (1-ß) are not significantly affected. (p. 424)

t test of hypothesis for the mean: is used when dealing with numerical data and the population standard deviation (σ_x) is unknown and estimated form the sample data (S). This parametric procedure assumes that the distribution from which the sample is drawn can be approximated by the normal distribution. (p. 424)

test statistic for t distribution: (p. 424)

$$t_{n-1} = \frac{\overline{X} - \mu_x}{\dfrac{S}{\sqrt{n}}}$$

where S = sample standard deviation

Wilcoxon signed-rank test: used to test a parameter reflecting central tendency. It provides a nonparametric alternative to the single population (one sample) t test or the paired (related samples) t test. (p. 430)

difference score (D_i):

a) $D_i = X_i - M$, where M = median for the single population (one sample) test;

b) $D_i = X_{1i} - X_{2i}$, where X_{1i} and X_{2i} are the ith observations from sample 1 and sample 2 respectively for the paired sample test. (p.431)

The Wilcoxon test statistic is obtained with the following formula:

$$W = \sum_{i=1}^{n} R_i^+$$

where R_i^+ = sum of the plus ranks. (p. 432)

chi-square distribution: a skewed distribution whose shape depends solely on the number of degrees of freedom. (p. 438)

chi-square test for a single variance: If the variable is assumed to be normally distributed, then the test statistic for testing whether or not the population value is equal to a specified value is given by the following: (p. 437)

$$\chi_{n-1}^2 = \frac{(n-1)\,S^2}{\sigma_x^2}$$ where σ_x^2 = hypothesized population variance
S^2 = sample variance
n = sample size

Wald-Wolfowitz one sample runs test for randomness: a method for testing whether the sequence of occurrence of a given set of observations results in a random pattern (p. 442)

a run: a consecutive series that is bounded by items of a different type or by the beginning or ending of the sequence. (p. 443)

trend effect: indicates a steady, gradual growth or decline for a given set of data. The null hypothesis of random pattern is rejected if there are too few runs. It usually involves interval (or higher) data and requires the calculation of the median.
(p. 443)

periodic effect: indicates changes in a data set occurring in a systematic fashion over time. The null hypothesis of random pattern is rejected if there are too many runs. It usually involves interval (or higher) data and requires the calculation of the median. (p. 444)

large sample approximation for the Wald-Wolfowitz one sample runs test: When the sample size n is greater than 40, the test statistic U is approximately normally distributed. Therefore when (n > 40) a large sample normal approximation is used. (p. 446)

156

REVIEW QUESTIONS

1. What are the advantages and disadvantages of using nonparametric and distribution-free methods?

2. Under what conditions is it appropriate to use a distribution-free test in lieu of a classical test?

3. What levels of measurement are required for most of the nonparametric tests?

4. When is it likely that the power of a parametric test is greater than the power of its nonparametric counterpart?

5. Under what conditions will the power of a nonparametric test exceed the power of its parametric counterpart?

6. Under what circumstances would it be appropriate to test a hypothesis of single mean using the student's t distribution in lieu of the standard normal distribution?

7. What assumption is made when using the chi-square test for a single variance and why is this assumption so critical to the accuracy of the test?

MULTIPLE CHOICE AND FILL IN QUESTIONS

1. Which one of the following is the most valid reason for the use of nonparametric test(s)?

a) they are used only in cases where classical tests do not exist

b) when nonparametric tests are available, they should always be chosen over their classical counterparts because they are more powerful

c) they are useful alternatives to classical tests when the assumptions underlying the classical counterpart test are not valid

d) a nonparametric test should never be used when its classical counterpart is available

e) none of the above

2. A set of numbers exhibit a non-random pattern if:

a) it contains too few runs.

b) it contains too many runs.

c) it contains either too many or two few runs.

d) the number of runs exceed [2n-1]/3.

3. All of the following are advantages of nonparametric methods except:

a) when all the assumptions of the classical procedures are met nonparametric methods are more powerful than their classical counterparts.

b) they are computationally less burdensome than their classical counterparts.

c) because they are usually based on ranks, they give less weight to extreme sample values (outliers) than their classical counterparts.

d) they make fewer, less restrictive assumptions than their classical counterparts.

4. The following is the order in which 14 consecutive items came of an assembly line. Defective items are denoted by D and nondefective items are denoted by N.

 NNDNNDDDNNDNNN

The number of runs present in these data are _____ .

5. The _____ test statistic is used in testing to see if a population variance is equal to a given hypothesized value.

(assuming an underlying normal population)

a) Z 　　　　　　　 b) t 　　　　　　　 c) χ^2

6. The _____ test statistic is used in testing the hypothesis for a single population mean is equal to a given hypothesized value if the population standard deviation is unknown.

a) Z 　　　　　　　 b) t 　　　　　　　 c) χ^2

7. Degrees of freedom for the chi-square single variance test

 is _____ .

a) n-1 　　　 b) n-2 　　　 c) n 　　　 d) none of the above

8. When testing the hypothesis for a single population mean if the population standard deviation is unknown, the probability of type II error (ß) depends on

a) the size of the sample.

b) the value of α (significance level).

c) the value of the standard deviation.

d) all of the above.

EXERCISES

1. A manufacturing firm believes that the vending machines located in the employees' lounge are not profitable because employees do not carry coins (nickels, dimes, quarters). Management believes that by installing a coin changer next to the vending machines, profit will improve. A coin changer will be installed if it is determined that employees carry an average of less than $0.50. To test their theory, 16 employees are asked how much change they are carrying. The sample mean is $0.42 and the sample standard deviation is $0.15. Should the coin changer be installed? (Assume a normal distribution, and use $\alpha = .05$).

2. A professional basketball player, Craig Lowdell, specializes in three point shots. During a practice, the assistant coach recorded his sequence of hits (H) and misses (M) of his shots from the three point range. The resulting sequence is given below. Can this sequence be considered random? Use a level of significance of .05.

H M H M H H M H H M H M H M M H M H

3. The production manager of Question 4 was also interested in the amount of variance in the time it took to fill orders. He estimated delivery time variance to be 2.5 days. A sample of 28 orders produced a sample variance of 3.4 days. Using α = .05, is the production manager's estimate correct?

4. Joe has been working as a salesperson for a direct-mail advertising company for the last five years. When he was hired, he had been told by the sales manager that he could expect to average **at least** two thousand dollars per month in sales commissions. It is believed that the monthly sales commissions are symmetrically but not normally distributed. A random sample of nine months of sales commissions for Joe had the following values. Is there evidence that the median sales commission is at least $2000. (Use α = .05.)

MONTHLY SALES COMMISSIONS

1700, 1500, 2200, 1800, 1950, 1400, 1600, 2300, 1700

5. A major retail chain's finance department at the local mall is evaluating the credit policy of its credit card users. The finance manager claims that the mean credit card balance is greater than $1000. To test this claim, he selected a random sample of 100 customers with credit cards, he found that the average sample balance is $1050 with a sample standard deviation of $250.

a) Can we conclude that the mean balance exceeds $1000? ($\alpha$ = .01)

b) If the same results (mean and standard deviation) were obtained using a sample of 144, would your conclusions be different? (α = .01)

c) Explain the affect of sample size on the power of the test.

ANSWERS TO REVIEW QUESTIONS

1. **Advantages** of the nonparametric tests over their classical counterparts include:

a) Nonparametric tests are easier to apply.

b) The calculations required by the nonparametric procedures are more quickly and easily done than those required by their classical counterparts.

c) Since the classical procedures have more restrictive assumptions, the data may not meet these restrictive assumptions about the distribution of the parent population(s) or the level of measurement.

d) If the assumptions of a classical procedure are not met, then its nonparametric counterpart is generally more powerful.

e) Nonparametric methods permit the solution of problems that do not involve a population parameter.

f) Nonparametric methods are generally more economical than classical procedures since the level of measurement and sample size requirements are not as restrictive.

Shortcomings of the nonparametric methods in comparison with their classical counterparts include:

a) For large samples, the calculations may become burdensome unless one uses approximations or computer software.

b) If the assumptions for a classical procedure are satisfied, using a nonparametric test in lieu of its classical counterpart will result in less power.

c) The special tables needed for the nonparametric procedures are not as readily available as the tables for the classical procedures.

2. They are useful alternatives to classical tests when the assumptions underlying the classical counterpart test are not valid (i.e. distribution and level of measurement). Also, nonparametric methods permit the solution of problems that do not involve a population parameter.

3. Many of the nonparametric tests require at least ordinal level of measurement, but some of them require only nominal level of measurement.

4. If the assumptions for a classical procedure are satisfied, the classical procedure will result in more power than its nonparametric counterpart.

164

5. If an assumption of the classical procedure is not met, then its nonparametric counterpart is generally more powerful.

6. The t distributions used when the population standard deviation is not known (is estimated), while the standard normal (Z) distribution is used when the population standard deviation is known. However, since the t distribution approaches the standard normal as the sample size increases, we can use the t distribution instead of the z distribution for large sample sizes.

7. The chi-square test of a single variance assumes a normal distribution. This test is sensitive to departures from normality and will affect the accuracy of the test, particularly if the sample size is small.

ANSWERS TO MULTIPLE CHOICE AND FILL IN

1. c   5. c
2. c   6. b
3. a   7. a
4. 7   8. d

SOLUTIONS TO EXERCISES

1. Hypothesis test for the mean (σ_x unknown) α = .05, n = 16, $\bar{x}$ = .42, s = .15

$H_0: \mu_x \geq .50$ $H_1: \mu_x < .50$

$$t_{n-1} = \frac{\bar{x}-\mu_x}{\frac{S}{\sqrt{n}}} = \frac{.42-.50}{\frac{.15}{\sqrt{16}}} = -2.13$$

test statistic = t = -2.13   critical value of t_{15} = -1.7531

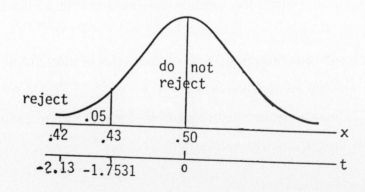

Because -2.13 falls in the rejection region, reject the null hypothesis.

The p value is less than alpha (.025 < .05).

The decision is to reject the null hypothesis - there is evidence that employees carry less than $0.50 in coins.

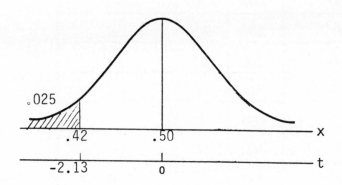

2. H_0: Random pattern $\qquad$ H_1: Nonrandom pattern

Reject H_0 at α = .05 if U ≤ 5 or U ≥ 15 (Table E.9.).

Since there are 15 runs (U = 15), we reject H_0 and conclude that his sequence of three point shots made or missed appears to be not random.

3. H_0: σ^2_x = 2.5 $\qquad$ H_1: $\sigma^2_x \neq$ 2.5

$$\chi^2_{n-1} = \frac{(n-1)S^2}{\sigma^2_x} = \frac{(28-1)3.4}{2.5} = 36.72$$

Lower critical value of χ^2_{27} = 16.151; upper critical value of χ^2_{27} = 43.194, 36.72 does not fall in the rejection region, do not reject the null hypothesis. $P(\chi^2$ for 27 degrees of freedom > 36.72) = .10. The p value is 2x.10 = .20 > .05, do not reject the hypothesis of equality. The production manager's estimate has been supported by the sample data (or there is no evidence that the estimate of 2.5 is not correct).

4. H_0: Median $\geq$ 2000 H_1: Median < 2000

Reject H_0 if $W \leq 8$ (Table E.10)

Sales	$D_i = X_i - M_0$	$|D_i|$	R_i	sign of D_i
1700	-300	300	5	-
1500	-500	500	8	-
2200	200	200	2.5	+
1800	-200	200	2.5	-
1950	-50	50	1	-
1400	-600	600	9	-
1600	-400	400	7	-
2300	300	300	5	+
1700	-300	300	5	-

$W = \Sigma R_i^+ = 2.5 + 5 = 7.5$

Since 7.5 is less than 8, we reject H_0 and conclude that the median sales commission appears to be less than $2000 per month.

5. Hypothesis test for a single mean standard deviation unknown

a) H_0: $\mu_x \leq 1000$ (the average credit card balance does not exceed $1000)

H_1: $\mu_x > 1000$ (the average credit card balance exceeds $1000)

$\alpha = .01$ critical value of t = $t_{99} = 2.3646$ (from table E.3.)

Reject H_0 if t > 2.3646.

$$t_{n-1} = \frac{\overline{x} - \mu_x}{\frac{S}{\sqrt{n}}} = \frac{1050 - 1000}{\frac{250}{\sqrt{100}}} = 2.00$$

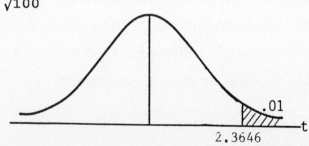

Since 2.00 < 2.3646, we don't reject the null hypothesis (H_0). There is no evidence to believe that the credit card balance for the customers exceed $1000.

b) H_0: $\mu_x \leq 1000$ (the average credit card balance does not exceed $1000)

H_1: $\mu_x > 1000$ (the average credit card balance exceeds $1000)

α =.01 critical value of t = 2.3528 (estimated from tbl. E.3)

Reject H_0 if t > 2.3528.

$$t_{n-1} = \frac{\overline{x} - \mu_x}{\frac{S}{\sqrt{n}}} = \frac{1050 - 1000}{\frac{250}{\sqrt{144}}} = 2.40$$

Since 2.40 > 2.3528, we reject the null hypothesis (H_0). There is significant evidence to believe that the credit card balance for the customers exceed $1000.

c) As we discussed in the previous chapter, increasing the sample size, increases the power of the test. The increased power is obtained because as the sample size increases, degrees of freedom for the t statistic increases and the critical value from the table gets smaller. In addition increased sample size results in a smaller standard error of the mean and as a result a larger calculated value of t. The combination of the two affects increases our ability to reject the null hypothesis, thus increasing the power of the test. We saw in part that we were not able to reject the null hypothesis with a sample of 100 customers. In part b when we increased the sample size to 144 customers holding everything else constant, t_{calc} increased, and the t_{table} decreased. These changes allowed us to reject the null hypothesis.

NOTES

CHAPTER 13

Two-Sample Tests with Numerical Data

CHAPTER SUMMARY

Confidence interval and hypothesis testing methods based on single samples were used to make statistical inferences about the population from which the sample is selected. More specifically, the confidence interval and the hypothesis testing methods of Chapters 11 and 12 involved making inferences about a single population mean (μ_X), median and a single population variance (σ^2_x).

A natural extension of the hypothesis testing procedures of Chapter 11 is to compare the parameters for two populations. For example, we may want to compare the average points scored by the Cleveland Browns with the average points scored by the Chicago Bears. The techniques presented in this chapter consist of parametric tests and distribution-free tests. Parametric (classical) tests are used to decide whether there are differences between two population means (dependent and independent samples) with either known or estimated standard deviations and differences between two population variances. All of the classical procedures in this chapter assume that the sampling distribution of the means of both populations can be approximated with the standard normal distribution. The chapter also presents distribution-free tests that are the counterparts of the two sample parametric procedures.

The distribution-free procedures are presented as alternatives to parametric (classical) procedures when the assumptions for the parametric procedures are not met.

KEY CONCEPTS AND TERMS

Choosing the appropriate test procedure when comparing two independent samples: select the most appropriate procedure for a given set of conditions so that the underlying assumptions are not violated. The criteria for selection includes the simplicity of the procedure, the generalizability of the conclusions to be drawn, the accessibility of tables of critical values for the test statistic, the availability of the computer software packages that contain the test procedure, and the statistical power of the procedure. (p. 462)

Testing the difference between the means of two independent populations having equal variances (variances are known): Since the population standard deviations are known, the following standard normal statistic is used to complete the test. (p. 463)

$$Z = \frac{(\overline{X}_1 - \overline{X}_2) - (\mu_1 - \mu_2)}{\sqrt{\dfrac{\sigma_1^2}{n_1} + \dfrac{\sigma_2^2}{n_2}}}$$

Testing the difference between the means of two independent populations when the variances are not known but assumed to be equal: In most cases, the population standard deviations are not known and must be estimated from a sample. (p.464) In these situations, the following t statistic is used:

$$t_{n_1+n_2-2} = \frac{(\overline{X}_1 - \overline{X}_2) - (\mu_1 - \mu_2)}{\sqrt{S_p^2\left(\dfrac{1}{n_1} + \dfrac{1}{n_2}\right)}}$$

where $S^2{}_p$, pooled variance of the groups, is determined using the following formula: (p. 464)

$$s_p^2 = \frac{(n_1-1)S_1^2 + (n_2-1)S_2^2}{(n_1 - 1) + (n_2 - 1)}$$

Behrens-Fisher problem: exists when two normally distributed independent populations from which the sample data is drawn do not have equal variances, therefore, the pooled variance estimate can not be used. (p.472)

Satterthwaite separate variance t, test for testing the difference between the means of two independent populations when the population variances are unknown and assumed to be unequal: used when the two populations have unequal variances. (p.472)

Testing the difference between the means of two independent populations when the variances are not known and are not equal: (p. 473)

$$t_{n_1+n_2-2} = \frac{(\overline{X}_1 - \overline{X}_2) - (\mu_1 - \mu_2)}{\sqrt{\frac{S_1^2}{n_1} + \frac{S_2^2}{n_2}}}$$

The separate variance t' test's table statistic value from the t table (Table E.3). The degrees of freedom for the t table can be approximated with the integer portion of the following computation.

$$\nu = \frac{\left(\frac{S_1^2}{n_1} + \frac{S_2^2}{n_2}\right)^2}{\frac{\left(\frac{S_1^2}{n_1}\right)^2}{n_1 - 1} + \frac{\left(\frac{S_2^2}{n_2}\right)^2}{n_2 - 1}}$$

Wilcoxon rank-sum test: is the nonparametric counterpart of the two sample t test. Individual observations in the smaller sample 1 of size n_1 and larger sample 2 of size n_2 are replaced by their combined ranks. (p. 481)

T_1 is the sum of the ranks assigned to the n_1 observations and T_2 is the sum of the ranks assigned to the n_2 observations. The critical values of the test statistic is given in Table E.11.

Testing the difference between the variances of two independent populations: The test statistic is based on the ratio of two sample variances. Assuming that the distributions from which the samples are selected have normal distributions, the ratio of the two sample variances follow the **F distribution**.

The test statistic can be stated as: (p. 489)

$$F_{(n_1-1),(n_2-1)} = \frac{S_1^2}{S_2^2}$$

Testing the difference between the means of two dependent related populations: The dependence occurs because the observations in the two samples are either **paired** according to some characteristic or **repeated measurements** are obtained from the same set of items. In this problem σ_D represents the population standard deviation of the differences between the matched pairs and is usually not known. Since the population standard deviation (σ_D) must be estimated using the sample standard deviation (S_D), the test statistic follows a t distribution and is given by the following: (p. 506)

$$t_{n-1} = \frac{\overline{D} - \mu_D}{\frac{S_D}{\sqrt{n}}}$$

where

$$S_D^2 = \frac{\sum\limits_{i=1}^{n} D_i^2 - \frac{\left(\sum\limits_{i=1}^{n} D_i\right)^2}{n}}{n-1}$$

$$\overline{D} = \frac{\sum\limits_{i=1}^{n} D_i}{n} \quad (average\ difference)$$

Two sample Wilcoxon signed-ranks test: it is used to test the difference between medians from two related samples. It is an extension of the one sample Wilcoxon signed-rank test of chapter 12. It is a distribution-free test and is used when the assumptions for its parametric counterpart (two related sample t test) are violated. (p. 511)

REVIEW QUESTIONS

1. What is the difference between the test of means for two independent populations vs. the test of means for two related populations?

2. List the assumptions about the population of interest when we use the Z test and compare it with the assumptions made in using the t test?

3. What is the difference between the Wilcoxon signed-rank test and the Wilcoxon rank-sum test?

MULTIPLE CHOICE AND FILL IN QUESTIONS

1. In testing the hypothesis for the difference between the means of two independent populations, the variances of the two samples can be pooled if the population variances are assumed to be _____.

2. In testing the hypothesis for the difference between the means of two independent samples, the ____ statistic is used if the standard deviation of each population is known.

3. If the variances of the two populations are not equal, the critical value of the t statistic is obtained by calculating an estimated degrees of _____.

4. In testing for the equality of variances from two independent populations the _____ test statistic is used.

a) t   b) F   c) Z   d) none of the above

5. The F statistic can sometimes assume negative values.

a) true   b) false

6. In testing the difference between two means from two normally distributed independent populations, the pooled estimate of the variance is used if the:

a) sample sizes are equal.

b) population variances are assumed to be equal.

c) variances of both populations are known.

d) sample sizes are large.

7. In testing the hypothesis for the difference between the means of two independent samples, the two sample sizes do not have to be equal to be able to use the Z statistic.

a) true   b) false

8. In testing for the equality of variances from two independent populations, if the null hypothesis is false, the test could result in:

a) a Type I error.

b) either a Type I error or a Type II error.

c) neither a Type I error nor a Type II error.

d) a Type II error.

e) both a Type I error and a Type II error.

9. There are two types of machines that can be used to complete a certain job. The production supervisor wants to determine which machine is more efficient. He assigns each of the 15 workers to both types of machines to compare the output per hour of the 15 workers. These two samples are:

a) dependent   b) independent

10. A statistician for the Skies and Wings (SW) airline company wishes to find evidence that the major competitor's average domestic air fare prices are higher than her company's. The alternative hypothesis is:

a) $\mu_{competitor} = \mu_{SW}$

b) $\mu_{competitor} \neq \mu_{SW}$

c) $\mu_{competitor} > \mu_{SW}$

d) $\mu_{competitor} < \mu_{SW}$

e) $\mu_{competitor} \geq \mu_{SW}$

11. In testing the difference between the two means from two normally distributed independent populations, the distribution of the difference in sample means will be:

a) normally distributed only if sample sizes are equal.

b) normally distributed only if both population standard deviations are known.

c) normally distributed.

d) normally distributed only if both sample sizes are very large.

e) normally distributed only if both population variances are equal.

12. The Wilcoxon rank-sum test is the nonparametric counterpart of the paired t test.

a) true   b) false

13. When using the Wilcoxon signed-rank test to compare two population medians, the test statistic "W" is computed by summing the signed ranks. In this computation, if we encounter tied absolute differences, they are:

a) assigned the average value of the corresponding ranks.

b) discarded and the sample size is reduced accordingly.

c) given the rank associated with the population median.

d) given the rank of the larger position.

e) none of the above.

14. For the Wilcoxon rank-sum test, as the number of observations in each sample becomes large, the distribution of the test statistic approaches the _____ distribution.

a) chi-square   b) student's t   c) binomial   d) normal

15. Which one of the following tests will always require more than nominal level of measurement?

a) chi-square goodness of fit test

b) chi-square independence test

c) Wald-Wolfowitz runs test

d) Wilcoxon signed-rank test

178

EXERCISES

1. The new coach of the Acorn University track and field team believes that his revolutionary training system can improve the performance of marathon runners. The mean time per mile (in minutes) for five of his runners before and after training is given below.

Runner	1	2	3	4	5
Mean time before training	5.88	7.48	6.12	6.84	8.01
Mean time after training	5.44	7.08	6.20	6.48	7.81

At α = .01, can we conclude that the coaches new training method significantly reduces the mean time per mile?

2. A test of the breaking strength of two different types of cables was conducted using samples of 16 pieces of each type of cable. The data are given in the following table. At the .10 level of significance, is there sufficient evidence to indicate a difference in the mean breaking strengths of the two cables? What bounds can we use to approximate p value for this problem? (Assume that the population variances are equal).

Cable 1	Cable 2
$\bar{X} = 1467$	$\bar{X} = 1445$
$s_1 = 40$	$s_2 = 30$

3. For the data in exercise two, assume that there is a reason to believe that the population variances are not equal. In addition, instead of randomly selecting 16 pieces of each cable, assume that 10 and 15 pieces of each cable are randomly selected. Everything else remains the same as in exercise two. At the .10 level of significance, is there sufficient evidence to indicate a difference in the mean breaking strengths of the two cables? Is there a difference in your answer in comparison to exercise two? Please carefully explain why?

4. A manufacturing engineer discovered a method of improving the efficiency in producing a certain chemical. However, he is concerned that the adjustments made to the production process would cause an increase in the variability of the output.
A random sample of 31 units before the adjustment indicated a standard deviation of 6.5 pounds. A random sample of 41 scores using the improved methodology indicated a standard deviation of 9.8 pounds. At a significance level of .01, is there evidence of a significant increase in the variability of the process after the change? Include a statement of conclusion and find the lower and upper limits on the p value.

5. An automobile manufacturing company is considering a switch to a different brand of a radial tire that is supposed to last longer. A random sample of 16 tires of the current brand and a random sample of 20 tires of the proposed brand was used to determine the average life of the tire (in years) for the current and the proposed brands. The sample mean life of the current brand was 3.3 years, while the sample mean life of the proposed brand was 4.2 years. The population standard deviations were known to be .80 and 1.0 years for the current and proposed brands respectively. At a significance level of .04, is there sufficient evidence to indicate that the average life of the tire for the current brand is shorter?

6. A random sample of 10 individuals are given a standardized math test before and after taking a course in mathematics. The scores are given below. These exam scores are not normally distributed. However, the distributions of the exam scores (before and after) are symmetric. At the .05 level of significance, is there any evidence that the course was helpful in improving the mathematics score on the standardized exam?

	Before	After
1	86	82
2	83	79
3	86	91
4	70	63
5	66	68
6	90	86
7	70	81
8	85	91
9	77	85
10	86	95

7. Two fastener vendors A and B supply a certain type of locknut called "stover locknut" for the assembly of automobiles. A random sample of 5 parts from A and 6 parts from B have the diameter measurements (in centimeters) given below. These measurements come from populations with non-normal distributions. Using a significance level of .10, do the data indicate a difference in the average diameter of the locknut between the two suppliers?

A	B
8.41	8.45
8.58	8.51
8.53	8.48
8.47	8.44
8.52	8.50
	8.49

ANSWERS TO REVIEW QUESTIONS

1. The test of means for two independent populations assumes that the variation due to other factors not being tested will average out due to random sampling. The test of means for two related populations match the observations between the two samples in order to reduce the variation attributable to individual observations and other factors. The dependent population test has very difficult data gathering requirements which, in some cases are impossible to satisfy.

2. **The major assumptions of the Z statistic**

   -- The samples are randomly selected;

   -- The sampling distributions of the population means are normal;

   -- The variances of both populations are known;

   -- The samples are independently gathered;

   -- The level of measurement is at least interval.

The major assumptions of the t statistic include:

   -- The samples are randomly selected;

   -- The sampling distributions of the population means are normal;

   -- The variance of the two populations are equal;

   -- The samples are independently or dependently gathered;

   -- The level of measurement is at least interval.

The main criteria for using the Z statistic is that the population variances are known and samples are independently collected. On the other hand, the t distribution is used when the population standard deviation is not known or the sample data represents pairing of observations rather than individually selected units from each population.

3. Both procedures are developed to test the difference between two medians. The Wilcoxon signed-rank test is used with two dependent samples, while the Wilcoxon rank-sum test is used with two independent samples.

ANSWERS TO MULTIPLE CHOICE AND FILL IN

1. equal	7. a	13. a
2. Z	8. d	14. d
3. freedom	9. a	15. d
4. b	10. c	
5. b	11. c	
6. b	12. b	

SOLUTIONS TO EXERCISES

1. H_0: $\mu_{before} - \mu_{after} \leq 0$ H_1: $\mu_{before} - \mu_{after} > 0$

Reject H_0 if $t_4 > 3.7469$

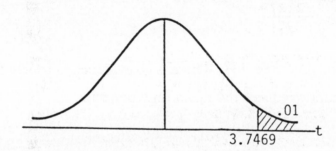

X_{before}	X_{after}	$D = X_1 - X_2$	D^2
5.88	5.44	.44	.1936
7.48	7.08	.40	.16
6.12	6.20	-.08	.0064
6.84	6.48	.36	.1296
8.01	7.81	.20	.04

$\sum D_i = 1.32$ $\sum D_i^2 = .5296$ $n = 5$

186

$$S_D^2 = \frac{\sum\limits_{i=1}^{n} D_i^2 - \dfrac{\left(\sum\limits_{i=1}^{n} D_i\right)^2}{n}}{n-1} = \frac{.5296 - \dfrac{(1.32)^2}{5}}{4} = .04528$$

$$\overline{D} = \frac{\sum\limits_{i=1}^{n} D_i}{n} = \frac{1.32}{5} = .264$$

$$s_D = \sqrt{.04528} = .21279$$

Therefore the test statistic is:

$$t_{n-1} = \frac{\overline{D} - \mu_D}{\dfrac{s_D}{\sqrt{n}}} = t_4 = \frac{.264 - 0}{\dfrac{.21279}{\sqrt{5}}} = 2.7742$$

Since 2.7742 < 3.7469, we don't reject H_0. There is no evidence to conclude that the coach's training method significantly reduces the mean time per mile.

2. $H_0: \mu_1 = \mu_2$ $\qquad\qquad$ $H_1: \mu_1 \neq \mu_2$

Reject H_0 if $t_{30} > 1.6973$ or $t_{30} < -1.6973$ (Table E.3.)

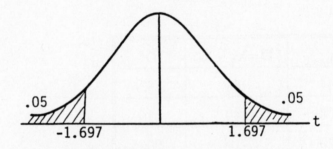

$$s_p^2 = \frac{(n_1-1)\,S_1^2 + (n_2-1)\,S_2^2}{n_1+n_2-2} = \frac{(16-1)\,(40)^2 + (16-1)\,(30)^2}{16+16-2} = 1250$$

$$t_{n_1+n_2-1} = \frac{(\bar{X}_1 - \bar{X}_2) - (\mu_1 - \mu_2)}{\sqrt{S_p^2\left(\frac{1}{n_1} + \frac{1}{n_2}\right)}} = \frac{1467-1445}{\sqrt{1250\left(\frac{1}{16}+\frac{1}{16}\right)}} \approx 1.76$$

Since 1.76 > 1.6973, we reject H_0 and conclude that there is a difference in the mean breaking strength of the two cables.

For the degrees of freedom = 30, the calculated t value of 1.76 falls between 1.6973 and 2.043 in Table E.3, therefore the p value is between .025 and .05 (in each tail) or .05 and .10 for a two tailed test.

3. Statement of the null and alternative hypothesis are the same as problem 2.

$n_1 = 10$ $\qquad\qquad\qquad n_2 = 15$

Reject H_0 if t > t_ν, where ν is computed with the following formula:

$$\nu = \frac{\left(\dfrac{S_1^2}{n_1} + \dfrac{S_2^2}{n_2}\right)^2}{\dfrac{\left(\dfrac{S_1^2}{n_1}\right)^2}{n_1-1} + \dfrac{\left(\dfrac{S_2^2}{n_2}\right)^2}{n_2-1}}$$

$$\nu = \frac{\left(\dfrac{(40)^2}{10} + \dfrac{(30)^2}{15}\right)^2}{\dfrac{\left(\dfrac{(40)^2}{10}\right)^2}{10-1} + \dfrac{\left(\dfrac{(30)^2}{15}\right)^2}{15-1}}$$

$$\nu = \frac{(220)^2}{\dfrac{(160)^2}{9} + \dfrac{(60)^2}{14}} = \frac{48400}{3101.5873} = 15.60 \approx 15$$

Reject H_0 if t > t_ν, where ν = 15 and t_{15} = 1.3406

$$t = \frac{(\bar{X}_1 - \bar{X}_2) - (\mu_1 - \mu_2)}{\sqrt{\dfrac{S_1^2}{n_1} + \dfrac{S_2^2}{n_2}}} = \frac{1467 - 1445}{\sqrt{\dfrac{1600}{10} + \dfrac{900}{15}}} = 1.4832$$

Since $1.3406 < 1.8135$, we do not reject H_0. We conclude that there is no evidence that the mean breaking strengths of the two cables differ.

Note that the answer we obtained for exercise three differs from the result of exercise two due to the differences in the equal variance assumption. In exercise two, it was assumed that the variances are equal. In exercise three, we did not assume that the variances were equal, as a consequence, our conclusion to problem three was more conservative. Therefore in exercise three, we were not able to reject the null hypothesis.

4. H_0: $\sigma^2_{new} \leq \sigma^2_{old}$ $\qquad\qquad$ H_1: $\sigma^2_{new} > \sigma^2_{old}$

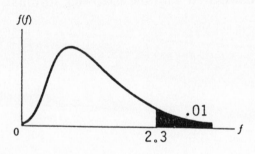

Reject H_0 if $F_{40,30} > 2.30$ (from table E.5)

Let the new method assume the subscript number 1 and let the old method assume the subscript number 2.

$$F_{(n_1-1),(n_2-1)} = \frac{S_1^2}{S_2^2} = \frac{(9.8)^2}{(6.5)^2} = 2.273$$

Since 2.273 < 2.30, we do not reject H_0 and conclude that there is no evidence of increased variability of the output.

$(.01 \leq p \text{ value} \leq .025)$

5. $H_0: \mu_{current} \geq \mu_{proposed}$ $\qquad$ $H_1: \mu_{current} < \mu_{proposed}$

Reject H_0 if $Z < -1.75$ (from table E.2)

Let the current brand assume the subscript number 1 and let the proposed brand assume the subscript number 2.

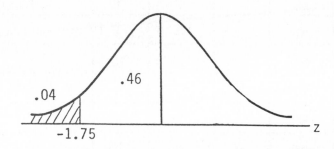

$$Z = \frac{(\overline{X}_1 - \overline{X}_2) - (\mu_1 - \mu_2)}{\sqrt{\dfrac{\sigma_1^2}{n_1} + \dfrac{\sigma_2^2}{n_2}}} = \frac{3.3 - 4.2}{\sqrt{\dfrac{(.8)^2}{16} + \dfrac{(1.0)^2}{20}}} = -3.0$$

Since -3 < -1.75, we reject H_0. There is sufficient evidence to indicate that the average life of the proposed brand is longer.

6. $H_0: M_D \leq 0$ $H_1: M_D > 0$

$D_i = X_{(after)i} - X_{(before)i}$

The critical value of the test statistic W for n = 10 and α = .05 is 45 (from Table E.10). Therefore reject H_0 if W > 45.

Ind.	before	after	D_i	$|D_i|$	R_i	sign of D_i
1	86	82	-4	4	3	-
2	83	79	-4	4	3	-
3	86	91	5	5	5	+
4	70	63	-7	7	7	-
5	66	68	2	2	1	+
6	90	86	-4	4	3	-
7	70	81	11	11	10	+
8	85	91	6	6	6	+
9	77	85	8	8	8	+
10	86	95	9	9	9	+

$$W = \sum_{i=1}^{n} R_i^+ = 5+1+10+6+8+9 = 39$$

Since 39 < 45, we don't reject H_0 and conclude that the course was not helpful in improving the mathematics score on the standardized exam.

7. H_0: $M_1 = M_2$ (the population median of the diameters of the locknuts from the two vendors are equal)

H_1: $M_1 \neq M_2$ (the population median of the diameters of the locknuts from the two vendors are not equal)

Reject H_0 if $T_1 \geq 40$ or $T_1 \leq 20$

T_1 is the sum of the ranks of the observations in the smaller sample.

A	R_1	B	R_2
8.41	1	8.45	3
8.58	11	8.51	8
8.53	10	8.48	5
8.47	4	8.44	2
8.52	9	8.50	7
		8.49	6

$T_1 = 1 + 11 + 10 + 4 + 9 = 35$

$T_2 = 3 + 8 + 5 + 2 + 7 + 6 = 31$

$T_1 + T_2 = 35 + 31 = [n(n+1)]/2 = [11(12)]/2 = 66$

Since $20 < 35 < 40$, we don't reject H_0 and conclude that there is not significant evidence to indicate that the median diameter of the locknuts differ between the two suppliers.

NOTES

CHAPTER 14

Analysis of Variance

CHAPTER SUMMARY

The basic concepts and techniques of statistical inference were covered in Chapters 10 through 13. Many of the ideas and skills learned in these chapters can be used in more advanced applications. In Chapter 13, we tested the differences between the means of two independent populations. This chapter discusses the test of the null hypothesis that several population means are equal.

First, a classical technique known as **Analysis of Variance (ANOVA)** is introduced to test for differences in the means of several groups (two or more). The chapter demonstrates the application of ANOVA procedures to three different experimental design models; completely randomized design, randomized block design, and a factorial design (two factors with multiple observations per each cell).

This chapter begins with the discussion of the one factor ANOVA (**completely randomized ANOVA**) comparing the means of several groups pertaining to one category (factor). This model provides a natural extension of the t test for comparing the means of two independent populations. Second, a distribution-free counterpart of the completely randomized ANOVA, namely Kruskall-Wallis test, is presented.

The later sections of the chapter are devoted to extending the one factor ANOVA to cases where the means for two factors are simultaneously compared. A distribution-free test option, entitled Friedman's test, for the two factor model is also presented.

KEY CONCEPTS AND TERMS

analysis of variance (ANOVA): partitions the total variation present in a data set into several groups where each group accounts for a specific source of variation. ANOVA determines the magnitude of the contribution of each of the sources to the total variation. (p. 527)

194

total variation (total sum of squares-SST): sum of the squared differences between each observation and an overall mean based on all the observations. (p. 529) It is computed as:

$$SST = \sum_{j=1}^{c} \sum_{i=1}^{n_j} (X_{ij} - \bar{\bar{X}})^2$$

where:

$$grand\ mean = \bar{\bar{X}} = \frac{\sum_{j=1}^{c} \sum_{i=1}^{n_j} X_{ij}}{n}$$

X_{ij} = ith observation in the j group

n_j = number of observations in group j

n = total number of observations

c = number of groups

The following computational formula for SST simplifies the manual calculations:

$$SST = \sum_{j=1}^{c} \sum_{i=1}^{n_j} X_{ij}^2 - \frac{(GT)^2}{n}$$

where:

$$GT = \sum_{j=1}^{c} \sum_{i=1}^{n_j} X_{ij}$$

within group variation: natural variability that can not be attributed to a specific cause. (p. 530) Within group variation is called sum of squares within (SSW) or **experimental error** and is given by the following formula:

$$SSW = \sum_{j=1}^{c} \sum_{i=1}^{n_j} (X_{ij} - \bar{X}_j)^2$$

where $\bar{X}_j$ is the mean of group j.

The following computational formula for SSW simplifies the manual calculations:

$$SSW = \sum_{j=1}^{c} \sum_{i=1}^{n_j} X_{ij}^2 - \sum_{j=1}^{c} \frac{T_j^2}{n_j}$$

where T_j is the sum of the values in group j.

among group variation: estimate of the variability among the population means. (p. 530) Between group variation is also called sum of squares between (SSA) and is given by the following formula:

$$SSA = \sum_{j=1}^{c} n_j (\overline{X}_j - \overline{\overline{X}})^2$$

The following computational formula for SSA eases the burden of computations:

$$SSA = \sum_{j=1}^{c} \frac{T_j^2}{n_j} - \frac{GT}{n}$$

SSA+SSW = SST

mean square within (MSW): measures the variability around the particular sample mean of each group. It is an estimate of a variance that measures the random variation of values within each group. (p. 530) MSW = SSW/n-c, where n-c is the degrees of freedom within (df_w).

mean square between (MSA): an estimate of the variance of observations between groups. It includes random fluctuations between observations within groups as well as differences between groups. (p. 530)

MSA = SSA/c-1, where c-1 is the degrees of freedom between (df_A)

F distribution: used in ANOVA because it is based on the ratio of two variances. (p. 531)

In ANOVA, F statistic is used as a one-tailed test with the rejection region in the right tail.

$F_{df1,\ df2}$ = MSA/MSW

A summary table for analysis of variance is given below:

Source	Sum of squares	Degrees of Freedom	Mean Square (Variance)	F statistic
Between Groups	SSA	$df_A = c\text{-}1$	$MSA = SSA/df_A$	$F = MSA/MSW$
Within Groups	SSW	$df_W = n\text{-}c$	$MSW = SSW/df_W$	
Total	SST	$df = n\text{-}1$		

assumptions of ANOVA: (p. 539)

1. Each group sample is selected from a population that can be at least approximated by a normal distribution.

2. All of the within group variations are equal (homogeneous variances).

3. The observations (X_{ij}) are independent of each other.

Tukey-Kramer procedure: determines which of the c means are significantly different from each other. This is a **post-hoc** procedure since it is done after the null hypothesis to the completely randomized ANOVA is rejected or it is concluded that at least two of the population means differ from each other. This test assists us in determining where the differences lie. (p. 537)

Hartley's test for homogeneity of variance: tests the ANOVA's assumption of equal group population variances. (p. 540)

Kruskal-Wallis ranks test for c independent samples: is the nonparametric counterpart of the F test for completely randomized design and is an extension of the Wilcoxon rank-sum test. (p. 545)

Kruskall-Wallis test should be used in lieu of one-way ANOVA if the assumption of equal variances or normality is violated.

The test statistic for Kruskal-Wallis is determined by the following equation:

$$H = \left[\frac{12}{n(n+1)} \sum_{j=1}^{c} \frac{T_j^2}{n_j} \right] - 3(n+1)$$

where n = the total number of observations over the c samples;

n_j = the number of observations in the jth sample, $j = 1, 2, .., c$;

T_j^2 = the square of the sum of the ranks assigned to the jth sample.

Dunn's multiple comparison procedure: simultaneously compares the medians to determine which of the c medians are significantly different from each other. This procedure is similar to Tukey-Kramer procedure. However this **post-hoc** procedure is completed following a Kruskall-Wallis rank (KWR) test (when the null hypothesis for KWR test is rejected) instead of following a classical one way ANOVA procedure. (p. 549)

Test statistic for Dunn's procedure is as follows:

There is a significant difference between group j and group j' if

$$|\bar{R}_j - \bar{R}_{j'}| > critical\ range \quad \text{where } \bar{R}_j = \frac{T_j}{n_j} \text{ and } T_j \text{ is the total rank for group j.}$$

(In other words $\bar{R}_J$ is the average rank for group j).

$$critical\ range = Z_U \sqrt{\frac{n(n+1)}{12} \left(\frac{1}{n_j} + \frac{1}{n_{j'}} \right)}$$

Z_U is the critical value from a standardized normal distribution containing an area of $\alpha / c(c-1)$ in the upper tail.

$j = 1, 2, ..., c$. and c is the total number of groups.

Number of possible pairwise comparisons = $c(c - 1)/2$.

characteristics of randomized block design: (p. 558)

1. The data are classified according to two criteria (factors) called **treatments (A)** and **blocks (BL)**.

2. The primary purpose in using a block is to remove the sources of variation attributable to the blocking variable from the error term.

3. Each treatment must be applied to each block.

A summary table for the randomized block analysis of variance is given below. The definitional sums of squares formulas for the randomized block design can be obtained from the textbook.

The following computational formulas simplify the computations.

$$SST = \sum_{j=1}^{c} \sum_{i=1}^{r} X_{ij}^2 - \frac{(GT)^2}{n}$$

$$SSA = \sum_{j=1}^{c} \frac{X_{.j}^2}{r} - \frac{(GT)^2}{rc}$$

$$SSBL = \sum_{i=1}^{r} \frac{X_{i.}^2}{c} - \frac{(GT)^2}{rc}$$

$$SSE = \sum_{j=1}^{c} \sum_{i=1}^{r} X_{ij}^2 - \sum_{j=1}^{c} \frac{X_{.j}^2}{r} - \sum_{i=1}^{r} \frac{X_{i.}^2}{c} + \frac{(GT)^2}{rc}$$

where c and r represents the number of treatments (columns) and the number of blocks (rows) respectively.

Source	SS	Degrees of Freedom	Mean Square (Variance)	F statistic
Among Treatments	SSA	$df_A = c-1$	$MSA = SSA/df_A$	$F = MSA/MSE$
Among Blocks	SSBL	$df_{BL} = r-1$	$MSBL = SSBL/df_{BL}$	$F = MSBL/MSE$
Error	SSE	$df_E = (r-1)(c-1)$	$MSE = SSE/df_E$	
Total	SST	$df = rc-1$		

Comparing the randomized block design to the one-way design:

The comparison can be made by determining the estimated relative efficiency (RE) of the randomized block design as compared with the one-way design. (p. 567)

$$RE = \frac{(r-1)\ MSBL + r(c-1)MSE}{(rc-1)\ MSE}$$

RE times as many observations in each group would be needed in a one-way design to obtain the same power for comparison of group means as would be needed for the randomized block design.

Friedman test: is the nonparametric counterpart of the F test for a randomized block design. (p. 571)

In performing the Kruskall-Wallis ranks test, the combined ranks of all observations were determined. In performing Friedman's test, the observations are ranked within each of the n blocks. Therefore R_{ij} is the rank (from 1 to c, where c is the number of groups) associated with the ith block and the jth group.

The test statistic is:

$$F_R = \frac{12}{nc(c+1)} \sum_{j=1}^{c} R_j^2 - 3n(c+1)$$

Nemenyi's multiple comparison procedure: simultaneously compares the medians associated with the levels of a given factor to determine which of the medians are significantly different from each other. This procedure is similar to Dunn's procedure. It is completed following a Friedman's procedure (when the null hypothesis for Friedman's test is rejected). (p. 574)

Test statistic for Nemenyi's procedure is:

There is a significant difference between group j and group j' if

$$|\overline{R}_{.j} - \overline{R}_{.j'}| > critical\ range$$

where $\overline{R}_{.j} = \frac{R_{.j}}{n_j}$ and R_j is the total rank in group j.

(In other words $\overline{R}_{.j}$ is the average rank for group j).

$$critical\ range = Q_{U[c,\infty]} \sqrt{\frac{c(c+1)}{12r}}$$

$j = 1,2,...,c.$ and c is the total number of groups.

number of possible pairwise comparisons $= c(c - 1)/2$

$Q_{U[c,\infty]}$ is the critical value from a **Studentized range distribution** containing c and ∞ degrees of freedom (Table E.12).

two way analysis of variance with n observations per cell: used to test differences in the means of two factors of interest (A and B) simultaneously. There are n observations for each combination of the levels of factor A with the levels of factor B. (p. 577)

interaction: responses for particular combination of the two factors that are inconsistent with those expected when each factor is analyzed separately. (p. 525)

The definitional sums of squares formulas for the two way ANOVA with multiple observations per cell can be obtained from the textbook.

The following computational formulas simplify the computations.

$$SST = \sum_{j=1}^{c} \sum_{i=1}^{r} \sum_{k=1}^{n} X_{ij}^2 - \frac{(GT)^2}{rcn}$$

$$SSFA = \sum_{j=1}^{c} \frac{X_{.j.}^2}{rn} - \frac{(GT)^2}{rcn}$$

$$SSFB = \sum_{i=1}^{r} \frac{X_{i..}^2}{cn} - \frac{(GT)^2}{rcn}$$

$$SSAB = \frac{\sum_{j=1}^{c} \sum_{i=1}^{r} X_{ij.}^2}{n} - \sum_{j=1}^{c} \frac{X_{.j.}^2}{rn} - \sum_{i=1}^{r} \frac{X_{i..}^2}{cn} + \frac{(GT)^2}{rcn}$$

$$SSE = \sum_{j=1}^{c} \sum_{i=1}^{r} \sum_{k=1}^{n} X_{ijk}^2 - \sum_{j=1}^{c} \sum_{i=1}^{r} \frac{X_{ij.}^2}{n}$$

A summary table for the two way analysis of variance is given below:

Source	SS	Degrees of Freedom	Mean Square (Variance)	F statistic
Factor A	SSFA	$df_{FA} = r-1$	$MSFA = SSFA/df_{FA}$	$F = MSFA/MSE$
Factor B	SSFB	$df_{FB} = c-1$	$MSFB = SSFB/df_{FB}$	$F = MSFB/MSE$
Interaction	SSAB	$df_{AB} = (r-1)(c-1)$	$MSAB = SSAB/df_{AB}$	$F = MSAB/MSE$
Error	SSE	$df_E = rc(n-1)$	$MSE = SSE/df_E$	
Total	SST	$df = (rcn)-1$		

fixed effects model: inferences drawn are limited to the factor levels used in the study which represent all levels of interest for that factor. (p. 588)

random effects model: levels of a factor are sample levels randomly selected from the population of all possible levels. (p. 588)

mixed effects model: both random and fixed effects factors are included in one study. (p. 588)

REVIEW QUESTIONS

1. What is the purpose of Tukey-Kramer test?

2. What are the differences and similarities between the one way ANOVA and t test of means from two independent populations?

3. In solving a one way ANOVA problem, does rejection of the null hypothesis imply that all of the group means are different from each other?

4. List the assumptions of ANOVA.

5. What is the primary objective of the randomized block design?

MULTIPLE CHOICE AND FILL IN QUESTIONS

1. In a completely randomized (one way) analysis of variance problem the calculated F ratio will increase as:

a) the variability among the groups decreases relative to the variability within the groups.

b) the total variability increases.

c) the total variability decreases.

d) the variability among the groups increases relative to the variability within the groups.

2. In a completely randomized analysis of variance problem with c columns **the variance between columns** is equal to:

a) (total sum of squares) minus (sum of squares within columns).

b) (sum of squares between columns)/(n-c).

c) [(total sum of squares)minus(sum of squares within columns)]/c-1.

d) [(total sum of squares)minus(sum of squares within columns)]/n-c.

3. Which one of the following ANOVA techniques can be used to test for an interaction effect between two factors?

a) completely randomized design

b) randomized block design

c) two way analysis of variance with n observations per cell

d) none of the above

4. In a completely randomized ANOVA, other things equal, as the sample means get closer to each other the probability of rejecting the null hypothesis

a) decreases.   b) increases.   c)remains the same.

5. A researcher wants to test whether the average starting salaries differ among the recent graduates of nursing, engineering and business schools. Which one of the following procedures would be most appropriate?

a) chi-square test of independence

b) t test for differences in means of independent populations

c) t test for differences in means of dependent populations

d) analysis of variance

6. In a completely randomized analysis of variance problem, if H_0 is true, we would expect the F test statistic to have a value of ____ .

7. The degrees of freedom for the within group variation of a completely randomized design (one way) ANOVA test with 4 groups and fifteen sample observations per each group is:

a) 3   b) 56   c) 59   d) 14   e) 4

8. Hartley's test can be used to test which one of the following assumptions of ANOVA?

a) independence of observations

b) random selection of the samples from each population

c) equality of the population variances

d) normal distribution of each population

e) equality of the population means

9. Which one of the following is not an assumption of analysis of variance?

a) independence of observations

b) random selection of the samples from each population

c) equality of the population variances

d) normal distribution of each population

e) equality of the population means

10. After solving a problem using the randomized block design ANOVA approach, the same data is analyzed using the one way analysis of variance (blocking variable is ignored). If the null hypothesis of equal group means is _____ for the one way ANOVA, the null hypothesis of equal group means is _____ for the randomized block design.

a) rejected, rejected

b) not rejected, rejected

c) rejected, not rejected

d) not rejected, not rejected

11. The Friedman's procedure is analogous to which one of the following classical procedures.

a) paired t test

b) randomized block design ANOVA F test

c) completely randomized ANOVA F test

d) two way ANOVA F test with n observations per cell

e) t test for the comparison of two independent population means

11. The Kruskal-Wallis procedure is analogous to which one of the following classical procedures.

a) paired t test

b) randomized block design ANOVA F test

c) completely randomized ANOVA F test

d) two way ANOVA F test with n observations per cell

e) t test for the comparison of two independent population means

EXERCISES

1. The marketing manager of a large company is comparing the effectiveness of three regional sales managers from regions A, B and C respectively. The revenue obtained from new customers is one way of measuring the effectiveness of the three managers. In this study, the marketing manager randomly and independently selected four months of new sales revenue data for each of the three regional sales managers. Data are given below in terms of ten thousand dollars. It is believed that new sales revenues for each region are normally distributed and the population variances are equal. At the .05 level of significance is there evidence of a difference of effectiveness among the three regional sales managers? Monthly new sales revenue

A	B	C
11	6	15
7	7	18
9	9	14
13	16	17

2. A study was completed using one way analysis of variance. Differences among the three group means were tested with an equal sample size for each group. The resulting analysis of variance table is partially given below. The sample means for groups A, B and C were 4.2, 5.4 and 10.6 respectively. The sample standard deviation was .65 for group A, .81 for group B and 2.65 for group C.

Source	SS	df	MS	F
Among Groups	80			
Within Groups	48			
Total		14		

a) Complete the ANOVA table. Is there evidence of a significant difference among the three population means at a significance level of .01?

b) If the null hypothesis in part (a) is rejected, using a significance level of .01, determine which means significantly differ.

c) Test the assumption of equality of variances using a significance level of .01. Is there a potential problem with using ANOVA to analyze this data set? Why?

3. An experiment was conducted to determine the effects of three different chemical mixing methods and three different brands of a certain chemical used during the process on the strength of the final plastic product. Three observations were taken for each chemical mixing method/chemical brand combination. Measurements represent the tensile strength in pounds. Data are given below. Test all appropriate hypotheses at a significance level of .05 and carefully state all of your conclusions.

Mixing Methods						
			X	Y	Z	totals
	K		8	13	6	
			10	14	9	
			9	12	9	
	M		2	7	3	
			6	8	7	
Chemical Brands			7	9	5	
	N		4	9	9	
			8	6	9	
			9	12	6	
totals						

4. A research group is studying the effectiveness of three distinct teaching methods of mathematics. The group believes that the mathematical aptitude of the students is an important factor that may effect the results. Nine students are selected for this study. Based on a standard test, the research group is able to classify the students into three categories of high, medium and low mathematical aptitude. Three of the students have high mathematical aptitude while three have medium and three have low mathematical aptitude. One student from each aptitude category is randomly assigned to each teaching method so that there is only one student from each aptitude category in each class using a certain teaching method. In other words, the research group uses the mathematical aptitude as a blocking factor in determining the differences in the effectiveness of the teaching methods. After two weeks of teaching, a standard test is given to all of the students and the results are given below.

a) Is there evidence of a difference in the teaching methods. Does the blocking factor significantly affect the results? If there is a significant difference in the teaching methods, which ones differ? Comment on the sample size.

Teaching Methods					
		A	B	C	total
	high	84	95	92	
Math. Aptitude	medium	77	86	70	
	low	72	78	64	
	total				

b) Determine the relative efficiency of the randomized block design as compared with completely randomized design (one-way design) and interpret it.

5. The data below represent random samples of the daily noon time sales revenue (in thousands of dollars) from three local fast food restaurants A, B and C respectively. It has been known that the noon time sales at these restaurants have highly skewed (nonnormal distributions.

a) At a significance level of .10, is there evidence that the three local fast food restaurants differ in their median noon time sales revenues?

A	B	C
2.55	1.70	2.05
3.21	1.63	1.85
1.93	2.10	2.25
2.35	1.95	1.80
2.75	2.15	1.90
1.75	1.50	2.35
2.50	1.99	2.20

b) If there is evidence of a difference among the three restaurants' median noon time sales revenues, determine which restaurant's sales are superior to the others. (α = .10)

6. An ice cream company is conducting a taste test. It wishes to discover if the taste preferences of consumers for their four brands of ice cream tend to differ. Five randomly selected potential consumers are asked to rank the four brands (a rank of 1 represents most preferred and a rank of 4 represents least preferred). The results are given in the following table. At a significance level of .05, is there evidence of a significant difference among the consumers' taste preferences of the four brands of ice cream? If so, which brands are preferred?

Ice cream

	W	X	Y	Z
Taster 1	1	3	4	2
Taster 2	1	2	3	4
Taster 3	1	2	4	3
Taster 4	2	1	3	4
Taster 5	2	1	4	3

ANSWERS TO REVIEW QUESTIONS

1. For an ANOVA problem, if a null hypothesis is rejected, then it is concluded that there is evidence that at least two of the group means significantly differ from each other. However, the rejection of the null hypothesis for the ANOVA is not able to show which of the group means significantly differ and which ones do not differ. Tukey-Kramer test can be used to determine specifically which of the means differ.

2. Both procedures involve the test of means. While the ANOVA procedure can be used to test differences among the group means for two or more samples, the t test of independent population means can only test the difference between two samples.

3. No. When the null hypothesis of equal means is rejected, we conclude that at least two of the means are significantly different from each other. However, we cannot identify which of the specific means differ. In order to identify specific differences, Tukey's multiple comparison procedure is used.

4. -- the observations (X_{ij}) are independent.

    -- the samples are randomly selected for each group

    -- the population variances are equal for each group

5. The primary objective of the randomized block design is to reduce the error variance (MSE) by removing from the SSE the variation that can be attributed to a secondary variable or factor called the blocking factor.

ANSWERS TO MULTIPLE CHOICE AND FILL IN

1. d	7. b
2. c	8. c
3. c	9. e
4. a	10. a
5. d	11. b
6. one	12. c

SOLUTIONS TO EXERCISES

1. H_0: $\mu_1 = \mu_2 = \mu_3$ H_1: some of the μ_j's are not equal

Reject H_0 if $F = MSA/MSW > F_{.05, 2, 9} = 4.26$ (table E.5)

(GT) $= 11 + 7 + 9 + 13 + 6 + 7 + 9 + 16 + 15 + 18 + 14 + 17 = 142$

$$SST = [(11)^2 + (7)^2 + (9)^2 + \ldots + (18)^2 + (14)^2 + (17)^2] - \frac{(142)^2}{12}$$

$$SST = 1876 - 1680.333$$

$$SST = 195.667$$

$T_1 = 11 + 7 + 9 + 13 = 40$ $T_2 = 6 + 7 + 9 + 16 = 38$

$T_3 = 15 + 18 + 14 + 17 = 64$

$$SSA = \left[\frac{(40)^2}{4} + \frac{(38)^2}{4} + \frac{(64)^2}{4} \right] - \frac{(142)^2}{12}$$

$$SSA = 1785 - 1680.333$$

$$SSA = 104.667$$

$$SSW = SST - SSA$$

$$SSW = 195.667 - 104.667$$

$$SSW = 91 \quad OR$$

$$SSW = [(11)^2 + (7)^2 + (9)^2 + (18)^2 + \ldots + (17)^2] - \left[\frac{(40)^2}{4} + \frac{(38)^2}{4} + \frac{(64)^2}{4} \right]$$

$$SSW = 1876 - 1785$$

$$SSW = 91$$

Source	SS	df	MS	F
Among Groups	104.667	2	52.333	5.1758
Within Groups	91.00	9	10.111	
Total	195.667	11		

Since $5.1758 > 4.26$, we reject H_0 and conclude that the average new sales revenues differ between at least two of the three regional sales managers.

2. a)

Source	SS	df	MS	F
Among Groups	80	2	40	10
Within Groups	48	12	4	
Total	128	14		

Since $10 > F_{.01,2,12} = 6.93$. At $\alpha = .01$, there is evidence of a significant difference between some of the three population means.

b) Since $n = 14 + 1 = 15$, the number of observations per group, $n_j = 15/3 = 5$.

$$critical\ range = Q_{\alpha,c,n-c}\sqrt{\frac{MSW}{n_j}}$$

$$Q_{.01,3,12} = 5.04\ (Table\ E.12)$$

$$critical\ range = (5.04)\sqrt{\frac{4}{5}} = 5.04(.894) = 4.506$$

$|\bar{X}_1 - \bar{X}_3| = |4.2 - 10.6| = 6.4 > 4.506$

$|\bar{X}_1 - \bar{X}_2| = |4.2 - 5.4| = 1.2 < 4.506$

$|\bar{X}_2 - \bar{X}_3| = |5.4 - 10.6| = 5.2 > 4.506$

It appears that only (mean 1 - mean 3) and (mean 2 - mean 3) significantly differ from each other. Mean 1 and mean 2 do not appear to differ significantly from each other.

c) $H_o: \sigma_1^2 = \sigma_2^2 = \sigma_3^2$ $\qquad$ H_1: not all σ_j^2 are equal $\bar{n} = \frac{15}{3} = 5$

$Reject\ H_0\ if\ F_{max[c,(\bar{n}-1)]} = F_{max(3,4)} > 37.0\ (Table\ E.8)$

$$F_{max(3,3)} = \frac{s_{max}^2}{s_{min}^2} = \frac{2.65^2}{.65^2} = 16.56$$

Since $16.56 < 37$, we would not reject H_0, and we would conclude that there is no evidence of a difference in the variances of the three groups.

3. H_{01}: $\mu_{1..}$ = $\mu_{2..}$ = $\mu_{3..}$ H_{11}: not all $\mu_{i..}$ are equal

   H_{02}: $\mu_{.1.}$ = $\mu_{.2.}$ = $\mu_{.3.}$ H_{12}: not all $\mu_{.j.}$ are equal

   H_{03}: AB_{ij} = 0   (for all i and j) H_{13}: some $AB_{ij} \neq 0$

$$\sum_{i=1}^{r}\sum_{j=1}^{c}\sum_{k=1}^{n} X_{ijk}^2 = 8^2 + 10^2 + 9^2 + \ldots + 9^2 + 9^2 + 6^2$$

$$\sum_{i=1}^{r}\sum_{j=1}^{c}\sum_{k=1}^{n} X_{ijk}^2 = 1938$$

$$GT = \sum_{i=1}^{r}\sum_{j=1}^{c}\sum_{k=1}^{n} X_{ijk} = 216$$

$$\frac{(GT)^2}{rcn} = \frac{(216)^2}{(3)(3)(3)} = 1728$$

SST = 1938 - 1728 = 210

$X_{11.}$ = 27 $X_{21.}$ = 15 $X_{31.}$ = 21

$X_{12.}$ = 39 $X_{22.}$ = 24 $X_{32.}$ = 27

$X_{13.}$ = 24 $X_{23.}$ = 15 $X_{33.}$ = 24

$X_{1..}$ = 90 $X_{.1.}$ = 63

$X_{2..}$ = 54 $X_{.2.}$ = 90

$X_{3..}$ = 72 $X_{.3.}$ = 63

$$\sum_{j=1}^{c} \frac{X_{.j.}^2}{rn} = \frac{(63)^2 + (90)^2 + (63)^2}{(3)(3)} = 1782$$

SSFA = 1782 - 1728 = 54

SSFB = 1800 - 1728 = 72

$$\sum_{i=1}^{r} \sum_{j=1}^{c} X_{ij\cdot}{}^2 = \frac{27^2 + 39^2 + 24^2 + 15^2 + 24^2 + \ldots +24^2}{3}$$

$$\sum_{i=1}^{r} \sum_{j=1}^{c} X_{ij\cdot}{}^2 = \frac{5598}{3} = 1866$$

SSAB = 1866 - 1800 - 1782 + 1728 = 12

SSE = 1938 - 1866 = 72

or SSE = SST - SSFA - SSFB - SSAB

SSE = 210 - 54 - 72 - 12 = 72

Source	SS	df	MS	F
Factor A	54	2	27	6.75
Factor B	72	2	36	9.0
Interaction	12	4	3	.75
Error	72	18	4	
Total	210			

$df_{interaction}$ = (r-1)(c-1) = (3-1)(3-1) = 4

df_{error} = rc(n-1) = (3)(3)(2) = 18

Reject H_{01} if F > $F_{.05,2,18}$ = 3.55

Reject H_{02} if F > $F_{.05,2,18}$ = 3.55

Reject H_{03} if F > $F_{.05,4,18}$ = 2.93

Since 6.75 > 3.55, we may reject H_{01}. There is evidence of a difference in the average tensile strength of the product between some of the mixing methods.

Since 9.0 > 3.55, we may reject H_{02}. There is significant evidence of a difference in the average tensile strength of the product between some of the chemical brands.

Since .75 < 2.93, we don't reject H_{03}. There appears to be no significant interaction between the chemical brands and the mixing methods. In other words, the tensile strength for the combinations of the two factors (mixing methods and chemical brands) are consistent with the tensile strengths expected when each factor is analyzed separately.

4. $X_{.1} = 233$ $X_{.2} = 259$ $X_{.3} = 226$

   $X_{1.} = 271$ $X_{2.} = 233$ $X_{3.} = 214$

$$\sum_{j=1}^{c} \frac{X_{.j}^2}{r} = \frac{(233)^2 + (259)^2 + (226)^2}{3} = 57,482$$

$$\sum_{i=1}^{r} \frac{X_{i.}^2}{c} = \frac{(271)^2 + (233)^2 + (214)^2}{3} = 57,842$$

$GT = 84 + 95 + 92 + 77 + ... + 64 = 718$

$$\frac{(GT)^2}{(r)(c)} = \frac{(718)^2}{(3)(3)} = 57,280.444$$

$$\sum_{j=1}^{c} \sum_{i=1}^{r} X_{ij}^2 = (84)^2 + (95)^2 + (92)^2 + ... + (64)^2 = 58,134$$

$SST = 58134 - 57280.444 = 853.556$

$SSA = 57482 - 57280.444 = 201.556$

$SSBL = 57842 - 57280.444 = 561.556$

$SSE = 58134 - 57482 - 57842 + 57280.444$

$SSE = 90.444$

or

$SSE = SST - SSA - SSBL$

$SSE = 853.556 - 561.556 - 201.556 = 90.444$

$H_{01}: \mu_{.1} = \mu_{.2} = \mu_{.3}$ H_{11}: not all $\mu_{.j}$ are equal

$H_{02}: \mu_{1.} = \mu_{2.} = \mu_{3.}$ H_{12}: not all $\mu_{i.}$ are equal

Source	SS	df	MS	F
Teaching Method	201.556	2	100.778	4.46
Math Aptitude	561.556	2	280.778	12.4
Error	90.444	4	22.611	
Total	853.556	8		

Reject H_{01} if $F > F_{.05,2,4} = 6.94$

Since $4.46 < 6.94$, we do not reject H_{01}. We conclude that there is <u>not</u> sufficient evidence to indicate a significant difference between the teaching methods.

Reject H_{02} if $F > F_{.05,2,4} = 6.94$

Since $12.4 > 6.94$, we reject H_{02}. It can be concluded that there is a significant difference in the math scores between the three levels of math aptitude. Thus, we may conclude that the blocking has been effective in reducing the experimental error.

Since the null hypothesis for the teaching methods is not rejected, Tukey's method is not used. A larger sample size may permit us to detect the differences between the teaching methods.

b)

$$RE = \frac{(r-1) \; MSBL + r(c-1) MSE}{(rc - 1) \; MSE}$$

$$RE = \frac{2 \; (280.778) + 3(2)(22.611)}{(9 - 1) \; 22.611}$$

$$RE = \frac{697.222}{180.888} = 3.854$$

This means that 3.854 as many observations in each group would be needed in a one way ANOVA design to obtain the same power for comparison of group means as would be needed for the randomized block design.

5. H_0: $M_1 = M_2 = M_3$

H_1: Not all M_j's are equal (where $j = 1,2,3$)

Reject H_0 if the test statistic $H > \chi^2$ with two degrees of freedom.

degrees of freedom = number of groups (c) - 1 or (3-1).

For $\alpha = .10$, χ^2 with two degrees of freedom = 4.605 (Table E.4)

A	R_A	B	R_B	C	R_C
2.55	19	1.70	3	2.05	11
3.21	21	1.63	2	1.85	6
1.93	8	2.10	12	2.25	15
2.35	16.5	1.95	9	1.80	5
2.75	20	2.15	13	1.90	7
1.75	4	1.50	1	2.35	16.5
2.50	18	1.99	10	2.20	14

$T_A^2 = (19 + 21 + 8 + 16.5 + 20 + 4 + 18)^2 = (106.5)^2 = 11342.25$

$T_B^2 = (3 + 2 + 12 + 9 + 13 + 1 + 10)^2 = 2500$ and

$T_C^2 = (11 + 6 + 15 + 5 + 7 + 16.5 + 14)^2 = 5550.25$

$$H = \left[\frac{12}{n(n+1)} \sum_{j=1}^{c} \frac{T_j^2}{n_j} \right] - 3(n+1)$$

$$H = \left[\frac{12}{21(22)} \left(\frac{11342.25}{7} + \frac{2500}{7} + \frac{5550.25}{7} \right) \right] - [3(21+1)]$$

$$H = 5.957$$

Since 5.957 > 4.605, we reject H_0. There is sufficient evidence that the three local fast food restaurants differ in their median noon time sales revenues.

b) **Dunn's procedure:**

T_j is the total rank for group j.

Specifically,

$T_A = 19 + 21 + 8 + 16.5 + 20 + 4 + 18 = 106.5$

$T_B = 3 + 2 + 12 + 9 + 13 + 1 + 10 = 50$

$T_C = 11 + 6 + 15 + 5 + 7 + 16.5 + 14 = 74.5$

There is a significant difference between group j and group j' if

$|\overline{R}_j - \overline{R}_j| > critical\ range$

where $\overline{R}_J$ is the average rank for group j.

$$\bar{R}_j = \frac{T_j}{n_j}$$

$$\bar{R}_A = \frac{T_a}{n_A} = \frac{106.5}{7} = 15.21427$$

$$\bar{R}_B = \frac{50}{7} = 7.1429$$

$$\bar{R}_C = \frac{74.5}{7} = 10.6429$$

Z_U is the critical value from a standardized normal distribution containing an area of $\alpha/c(c-1)$ in the upper tail.

Upper tail of the standardized normal distribution is: $\frac{.10}{(3)(2)} = .0166$

Therefore, we find the probability of .4834 (.5 - .0166) in the body of the Z table (Table E.2) and read the corresponding value of Z. $Z_U = 2.13$.

$$critical\ range = 2.13 \sqrt{\frac{(21)(22)}{12}\left(\frac{1}{7} + \frac{1}{7}\right)}$$

$$critical\ range = 2.13 \sqrt{\frac{(462)}{12}(.2857))}$$

$$critical\ range = 2.13 \sqrt{11} = 7.06441$$

$|\bar{R}_A - \bar{R}_B| = |15.2143 - 7.1429| = 8.0714 > 7.0644$ (sig. difference)

$|\bar{R}_A - \bar{R}_C| = |15.2143 - 10.6429| = 4.5714 < 7.0644$ (no sig. diff.)

$|\bar{R}_B - \bar{R}_C| = |7.1429 - 10.6429| = 3.50 < 7.0644$ (no sig. diff.)

We can conclude that the median noon hour sales of restaurant A is higher than the median noon hour sales of restaurant B. There are no significant differences in the median noon hour sales between restaurant pairs B vs. C and A vs. C.

6. $H_0: M_1 = M_2 = M_3 = M_4$ H_1: Not all M_j's are equal (where $j = 1,2,3,4$)

Reject H_0 if $F_R > \chi^2$ with (4-1) degrees of freedom.

For $\alpha = .05$, χ^2 with 3 degrees of freedom = 7.815 (Table E.4)

Rank sums for each ice cream brand are given by:

$R_{.W} = (1+1+1+2+2) = 7$ $R_X = (3+2+2+1+1) = 9$ $R_{.Y} = (4+3+4+3+4) = 18$

$R_{.Z} = (2+4+3+4+3) = 16$

$$F_R = \frac{12}{nc(c+1)} \sum_{j=1}^{c} R_j^2 - 3n(c+1)$$

$$F_R = \frac{12}{5(4)(5)} (7^2 + 9^2 + 18^2 + 16^2) - [3(5)(4+1)]$$

$$F_R = 10.2$$

Since 10.2 is > 7.815, we reject H_0. We may conclude that there are significant differences with respect to the consumers' preferences among some of the four brands of ice cream.

Nemenyi's multiple comparison procedure:

Rank sums: $R_{.W} = 7$ $R_X = 9$ $R_{.Y} = 18$ $R_Z = 16$

Average ranks: $\bar{R}_{.w} = 1.4$ $\bar{R}_{.x} = 1.8$ $\bar{R}_Y = 3.6$ $\bar{R}_Z = 3.2$

For example the average rank for ice cream brand W is computed as:

$$\bar{R}_{.w} = \frac{R_{.w}}{r} = \frac{7}{5} = 1.4$$

The average rank for the other ice cream brands are calculated in a similar fashion.

Upper tail of the studentized range Q for α level of .05 is:

$$Q_{(c,\infty)} = Q_{(4,\infty)} = 3.63$$

There is a significant difference between group j and group j' if

$$|\bar{R}_{.j} - \bar{R}_{.j}| > critical\ range$$

$$critical\ range = Q_{U[c,\infty]} \sqrt{\frac{c(c+1)}{12r}}$$

$$critical\ range = 3.63 \sqrt{\frac{(4)(5)}{(12)(5)}}$$

$$critical\ range = 3.63 \sqrt{.333}$$

$$critical\ range = 2.0957$$

Number of comparisons $= c(c-1)/2 = (4)(3)/(2) = 6$

$| \bar{R}_{.w} - \bar{R}_{.x} | = | 1.4 - 1.8 | = .4 < 2.0957$ (no significant difference)

$| \bar{R}_{.w} - \bar{R}_{.y} | = | 1.4 - 3.6 | = 2.2 > 2.0957$ (no significant difference)

$| \bar{R}_{.w} - \bar{R}_{.z} | = | 1.4 - 3.2 | = 1.8 < 2.0957$ (no significant difference)

$| \bar{R}_{.x} - \bar{R}_{.y} | = | 1.8 - 3.6 | = 1.8 < 2.0957$ (no significant difference)

$| \bar{R}_{.x} - \bar{R}_{.z} | = | 1.8 - 3.2 | = 1.4 < 2.0597$ (no significant difference)

$| \bar{R}_{.y} - \bar{R}_{.z} | = | 3.6 - 3.2 | = 0.4 < 2.0957$ (no significant difference)

Since the second pairwise comparison exceeds the critical value, we can conclude that the consumers appear to prefer ice cream brand W over ice cream brand Y. However, there is no evidence of a difference in the consumer taste preferences between any other pairs of ice cream brands.

CHAPTER 15

Hypothesis Testing With Categorical Data

CHAPTER SUMMARY

All of the hypotheses tests that have been covered so far were designed to analyze numerical data. Often it is necessary to determine if differences exist in categorical data or if there are relationships among categorical variables. The analysis of one, two or several categorical variables is the topic of this chapter.

The chapter begins with one and two sample Z tests for proportions. The chi-square test is presented for two proportions, multiple proportions and tests of independence. Should the chi-square test reject the null hypothesis of equality of proportions, the Marascuilo procedure is provided as a post-hoc comparison test to determine which proportions are different. And finally, the McNemar test is included as a test of differences for two related proportions.

KEY CONCEPTS AND TERMS

one sample Z test for the proportion: (p. 606)

proportion of successes in the sample

$$Z \approx \frac{p_s - p}{\sqrt{\dfrac{p(1-p)}{n}}}$$

where $p_s = \dfrac{x}{n}$ = observed proportion of successes

p = proportion of successes from the null hypothesis

number of successes in the sample

$$Z \approx \frac{X - np}{\sqrt{np(1-p)}}$$

where X = the number of successes in the sample

p = proportion of successes from the null hypothesis

Z test for differences in two proportions (independent samples): (p. 611)

$$Z = \frac{(p_{s_1} - p_{s_2}) - (p_1 - p_2)}{\sqrt{\overline{p}(1-\overline{p})\left(\frac{1}{n_1} + \frac{1}{n_2}\right)}} \qquad \overline{p} = \frac{X_1 + X_2}{n_1 + n_2}$$

where P_{s_1} = sample proportion obtained from population 1 (x_1/n_1)

P_{s_2} = sample proportion obtained from population 2 (x_2/n_2)

X_1 = number of successes in sample 1

X_2 = number of successes in sample 2

n_1 = size of sample taken from population 1

n_2 = size of sample taken from population 2

$\overline{p}$ = pooled estimate of the population proportion

chi-square test for differences in two proportions (independent samples): (p. 619)

$$\chi^2 = \sum_{all\ cells} \frac{(f_o - f_e)^2}{f_e}$$

where f_o = observed frequency in each cell

f_e = expected frequency in each cell

Marascuilo procedure: (p. 628)

$$critical\ range = \sqrt{\chi^2_{U(c-1)}} \sqrt{\frac{P_{s_j}(1-P_{s_j})}{n_j} + \frac{P_{s_{j'}}(1-P_{s_{j'}})}{n_{j'}}}$$

where $\sqrt{\chi^2_{U(c-1)}}$ = the square root of the uppertailed critical value from a chi-square distribution having c-1 degrees of freedom

chi-square test of independence: (p. 632)

$$\chi^2 = \sum_{all\ cells} \frac{(f_o - f_e)^2}{f_e}$$

where f_o = observed frequency in each cell

f_e = expected frequency in each cell

$$f_e = \frac{row\ sum\ \times\ column\ sum}{n}$$

where row sum = the sum of all the frequencies in the row

column sum = the sum of all the frequencies in the column

n = sample size

McNemar test: a test for the difference between proportions from two related populations. (p. 644)

$$Z = \frac{B-C}{\sqrt{B+C}} \qquad P_{s_1} = \frac{A+B}{n} \qquad P_{s_2} = \frac{A+C}{n}$$

where A = number of participants with "positive" responses to condition 1 and "positive" responses to condition 2

B = number of participants with "positive" responses to condition 1 and "negative" responses to condition 2

C = number of participants with "negative" responses to condition 1 and "positive" responses to condition 2

D = number of participants with "negative" responses to condition 1 and "negative" responses to condition 2

P_{s_1} = proportion of respondents in the sample who answer yes to condition 1

P_{s_2} = proportion of respondents in the sample who answer yes to condition 2

REVIEW QUESTIONS

1. When using the normal approximation to test the difference between proportions of independent populations, why are the proportions pooled?

2. What are the hypotheses for the chi-square test of independence?

3. In what situation should you use McNemar's test rather than a chi-square test for the difference between proportions?

4. Why is the chi-square test of independence and the test for differences of proportions always a one-tailed test?

5. What two methods can be used to test the difference between two proportions and what are the advantages of each method?

6. What is the purpose of the Marascuilo test?

MULTIPLE CHOICE AND FILL IN QUESTIONS

1. Degrees of freedom for the chi-square test of independence is _____.

2. In testing the equality of proportions using both Z and χ^2, if Z = 2.3, the value of χ^2 would be _____.

3. A test for a single proportion can be done by analyzing the _____ of successes in the sample or the _____ of successes in the sample.

4. In testing the difference between two proportions, the normal distribution and the chi-square test are equivalent. However, if directional difference is important (i.e., $p_1 > p_2$), the chi-square test must be used.
a) true   b) false

5. The test statistic in the McNemar test is approximately _____ distributed and should be compared to a _____ table.

6. The McNemar test can be a one or a two tailed test.
a) true   b) false

7. Chi-square tests of independence require a minimum of _____ observations in each cell of the contingency table.

EXERCISES

1. Before test marketing a new flavored toothpaste, the consumer products division wants evidence that more than 60% of consumers will like the new taste. Survey data indicated that 160 out of the 250 respondents liked the new flavor. Is this sufficient evidence to begin test marketing? Use $\alpha = .05$.

2. Data has been collected to determine if railroads are sensitive to the needs of their shippers. Shippers require early delivery of priority freight (before noon) but have no such requirement of general freight. Therefore, railroads should be scheduling more priority trains for early arrival and more general freight trains for late arrival (after noon). Use the following data to determine if there is a difference in arrival times for the two types of freight ($p_1 = p_2$). Use the normal distribution and $\alpha = .05$.

Priority Freight	General Freight
$n_1 = 85$	$n_2 = 128$
$X_1 = 55$	$X_2 = 54$

where X_i = number of trains scheduled for early arrival.

3. The railroad data of Question 2 can be converted to a 2 x 2 contingency table. Use the second method of analysis, chi-square test, to test the hypothesis of Question 2.

	Priority	General	Totals
Early Arrival	55	54	109
Late Arrival	30	74	104
Totals	85	128	213

4. A particular railroad has two additional service designations for freight delivery and has provided the following data. Is there a difference in arrival times for the four types of freight ($p_1 = p_2 = p_3 = p_4$)? $\alpha = .05$

	Priority One	Priority Two	Priority Three	General	Totals
Early Arrival	48	68	42	52	210
Late Arrival	2	12	98	128	240
Totals	50	80	140	180	450

5. If there is a significant difference in arrival times in problem 4, test to determine which types of freight are different. $\alpha = .05$

6. Believing that orders were taking too long to be filled, the production manager instituted a new inventory system. Data was collected from each of their customers, both before and after the new system went into effect. Based on this data, is there evidence of a difference in on-time delivery between the old and new systems? ($\alpha = .05$)

After New Inventory System

Before New Inventory System	On-time Delivery	Late Delivery
On-time Delivery	18	5
Late Delivery	24	17

ANSWERS TO REVIEW QUESTIONS

1. The pooled estimate for the population proportion is based on the null hypothesis of equality. The null hypothesis assumes that the two population proportions are equal.

2. H_0: There is independence (no relation) between the variables

   H_1: There is a relationship (dependence) between the variables

3. McNemar's test should be used when the two proportions are from two related populations. For instance, before and after measurements taken on the same subjects would be related.

4. The chi-square test of independence and difference between proportions is based on the concept that for each cell the observed frequencies should equal the expected frequencies. These squared, weighted differences between observed and expected have an approximate chi-square distribution. Large differences result in large values of chi-square. The test is only concerned with the upper tail, the area representing large differences between observed and expected frequencies.

5. The Z test and the chi-square test can both determine differences in proportions. The advantage to using the Z test is in its ability to detect directional differences such as $p_1 > p_2$. The advantage to the chi-square test is that it can be used for comparing more than two proportions, however, the Z test can be used for no more than two groups.

6. The Marascuilo test is used for multiple comparisons. If a chi-square test indicates differences among proportions, we only know that not all of the proportions are alike. The Marascuilo test answers the question of exactly which proportions are different.

ANSWERS TO MULTIPLE CHOICE AND FILL IN

1. (r-1)(c-1)

2. $2.30^2 = 5.29$

3. proportion, number

4. a

5. normally, Z

6. a

7. five

SOLUTIONS TO EXERCISES

1. Hypothesis test for a proportion (one sample)

H_0: p ≤ .60

H_1: p > .60

α = .05, n = 250, p_s = 160/250 = .64, p = .60

$$Z \approx \frac{P_s - p}{\sqrt{\dfrac{p(1-p)}{n}}} = \frac{.64 - .60}{\sqrt{\dfrac{(.6)(.4)}{250}}} = 1.29$$

or

$$Z \approx \frac{X - np}{\sqrt{np(1-p)}} = \frac{160 - 250(.6)}{\sqrt{250(.6)(.4)}}$$

test statistic = Z = 1.29   critical value of Z = 1.645

Because the test statistic does not fall in the rejection region (1.29 < 1.645), do not reject the null hypothesis (H_0).

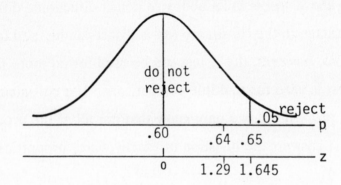

p value = .0985 which is greater than alpha (.0985 > .05)

Decision is to not reject the null hypothesis - there is no evidence to believe more than 60% of consumers like the new flavor and test marketing should not begin.

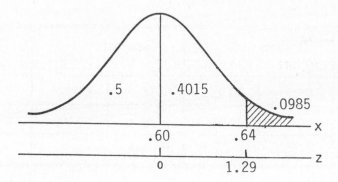

2. $H_0: p_1 = p_2$ $H_1: p_1 \neq p_2$

$$\bar{p} = \frac{x_1 + x_2}{n_1 + n_2} = \frac{55 + 54}{85 + 128} = .51$$

$$p_{s_1} = \frac{x_1}{n_1} = \frac{55}{85} = .65$$

$$p_{s_2} = \frac{x_2}{n_2} = \frac{54}{128} = .42$$

$$Z \approx \frac{(p_{s_1} - p_{s_2}) - (p_1 - p_2)}{\sqrt{\bar{p}(1-\bar{p})\left(\frac{1}{n_1} + \frac{1}{n_2}\right)}} = \frac{(.65 - .42) - 0}{\sqrt{.51(.49)\left(\frac{1}{85} + \frac{1}{128}\right)}} = 3.29$$

Critical value of $Z = 1.96$ test statistic = 3.29

3.29 falls in the rejection region, 3.29 > 1.96, reject the null hypothesis.

$P(Z > 3.29) = .5 - .4995 = .0005$

Because the p value = 2 x (.0005) = .001 < .05 = α, reject the null hypothesis of equality. It appears that there is a difference in arrival times for priority and general freight trains.

3.

$$\bar{p} = \frac{x_1 + x_2}{n_1 + n_2} = \frac{55 + 54}{85 + 128} = .51$$
$$(1 - \bar{p}) = .49$$

85(.51) = 43.35   128(.51) = 65.28

85(.49) = 41.65   128(.49) = 62.72

	Priority f_o	f_e	General f_o	f_e	Totals
Early Arrival	55	43.35	54	65.28	109
Late Arrival	30	41.65	74	62.72	104
Totals	85		128		213

$$\chi^2_{(r-1)(c-1)} \approx \sum_{all\ cells} \frac{(f_o - f_e)^2}{f_e}$$

$$= \frac{(55 - 43.35)^2}{43.35} + \frac{(54 - 65.28)^2}{65.28}$$

$$+ \frac{(30 - 41.65)^2}{41.65} + \frac{(74 - 62.72)^2}{62.72}$$

$$= 10.37$$

$$\chi^2_1 = 10.37$$

Critical value of $\chi^2_1 = 3.841$ 10.37 falls in the rejection region, reject the null hypothesis. Because $P(\chi^2 > 10.37) < .005$, and $.005 < \alpha = .05$, again the null hypothesis of equality is rejected. It appears that the arrival time of the trains is contingent upon the type of freight (priority or general).

4.

$$\overline{p} = \frac{x_1 + x_2 + x_3 + x_4}{n_1 + n_2 + n_3 + n_4} = \frac{48 + 68 + 42 + 52}{50 + 80 + 140 + 180} = .47 \qquad (1 - \overline{p}) = .53$$

$50(.47) = 23.3 \quad 80(.47) = 37.6 \quad 140(.47) = 65.8 \quad 180(.47) = 84.6$

$50(.53) = 26.5 \quad 80(.53) = 42.4 \quad 140(.53) = 74.2 \quad 180(.53) = 95.4$

$$\chi^2_{(r-1)(c-1)} \cong \sum_{all\ cells} \frac{(f_o - f_e)^2}{f_e}$$

$$= \frac{(48 - 23.5)^2}{23.5} + \frac{(68 - 37.6)^2}{37.6}$$

$$+ \frac{(42 - 65.8)^2}{65.8} + \frac{(52 - 84.6)^2}{84.6}$$

$$+ \frac{(2 - 26.5)^2}{26.5} + \frac{(12 - 42.4)^2}{42.4}$$

$$+ \frac{(98 - 74.2)^2}{74.2} + \frac{(128 - 95.4)^2}{95.4}$$

$$= 134.51$$

$$\chi^2_1 = 134.51$$

Critical value of $\chi^2_3 = 7.815$ 134.51 falls in the rejection region, reject the null hypothesis. Because $P(\chi^2 > 131.517) < .005$, and $.005 < \alpha = .05$, again the null hypothesis of equality is rejected.   It appears that the arrival time of the trains is contingent upon the type of freight (priority one, two, three or general).

5. While chi-square indicates a difference in arrival times, the Marascuilo test must be done to determine which freight types are different.

$$P_{s_1} = \frac{X_1}{n_1} = \frac{48}{50} = .96 \qquad P_{s_2} = \frac{X_2}{n_2} = \frac{68}{80} = .85$$

$$P_{s_3} = \frac{X_3}{n_3} = \frac{42}{140} = .30 \quad P_{s_4} = \frac{X_4}{n_4} = \frac{52}{180} = .29$$

$$\sqrt{X^2_{U(c-1)}} = \sqrt{7.815} = 2.8$$

$$|P_{s_1} - P_{s_2}| = |.96 - .85| = .14 \quad 2.8\sqrt{\frac{(.96)(.04)}{50} + \frac{(.85)(.15)}{80}} = .14$$

$$\left|P_{s_1} - P_{s_3}\right| = |.96 - .30| = .66 \quad 2.8\sqrt{\frac{(.96)(.04)}{50} + \frac{(.30)(.70)}{140}} = .13$$

$$\left|P_{s_1} - P_{s_4}\right| = |.96 - .29| = .67 \quad 2.8\sqrt{\frac{(.96)(.04)}{50} + \frac{(.29)(.71)}{180}} = .12$$

$$\left|P_{s_2} - P_{s_3}\right| = |.85 - .30| = .55 \quad 2.8\sqrt{\frac{(.85)(.15)}{80} + \frac{(.30)(.70)}{140}} = .16$$

$$\left|P_{s_2} - P_{s_4}\right| = |.85 - .29| = .56 \quad 2.8\sqrt{\frac{(.85)(.15)}{80} + \frac{(.29)(.71)}{180}} = .15$$

$$\left|P_{s_3} - P_{s_4}\right| = |.30 - .29| = .01 \quad 2.8\sqrt{\frac{(.30)(.70)}{140} + \frac{(.29)(.71)}{180}} = .14$$

There appears to be no difference between Priority one and Priority two nor between Priority three and General. The remainder of the comparisons are all significant at $\alpha = .05$.

6. $H_0: p_1 = p_2 \quad H_1: p_1 \neq p_2$

$$Z = \frac{B-C}{\sqrt{B+C}} = \frac{5 - 24}{\sqrt{5 + 24}} = -3.53$$

Critical value of $Z = -1.96$, -3.53 falls in the rejection region, reject the null ($-3.53 < -1.96$)
$P(Z < -3.53) = .5 - .49979 = .00021$
p value is $2 \times .00021 = .00042 < .05$, reject the null hypothesis of equality. The data supports a difference in proportions before and after the new inventory system.

CHAPTER 16

Statistical Applications in Quality
and Productivity Management

CHAPTER SUMMARY

As a result of increased global competition, a rapidly growing number of companies of all sizes are paying much more attention to issues involving quality and productivity. Many statistical techniques are available to assist organizations in improving the quality of their products and services. It is important for companies to use these techniques in the context of an overall quality system which requires quality awareness, careful planning and commitment at all levels of the organization. Many companies are not only utilizing these statistical techniques themselves, but are also requiring their suppliers to meet certain standards of quality, based on various statistical measures.

This chapter covers the statistical applications of quality control and the related managerial philosophy developed by W. Edwards Deming. Control charts are given the primary emphasis, but other quality control topics such as pre-statistical tools and inspection are also discussed.

KEY CONCEPTS AND TERMS

total quality management (TQM): it is a philosophy that focuses on quality, customer service, teamwork and continuous improvement of processes, products and services. (p. 661)

process: a sequence of steps that describe an activity from beginning to completion (p. 664)

control chart: a means of studying variation in a product or service by focusing on (1) the time dimension in which the system produces products or services and (2) capturing the variability in the system. It enables the user to study the behavior of variation in any system. (p. 662)

special cause of variation: variation due to an individual fluctuation. The objective is to identify the source(s) of variation and remove them from the process. (p. 662)

242

common causes of variation: variation due to the inherent variability in the process. It consists of the numerous small causes of variability that operate randomly or by chance. (p. 662)

Fishbone (Ishikawa)(cause and effect) diagram: depicts and organizes by major category the potential causes of the desired or the undesired effect. (p. 665)

process flow diagram: depicts the relevant steps of a process from beginning to termination using a series of symbols. (p. 666)

W. Edwards Deming: recognized as one of the top international leaders of modern quality management. His philosophy is based on improving manufacturing of products and delivery of services by reducing process variation and uncertainty. Statistical thinking is a major component of his philosophy. He advocates radical cultural change within the organization which is included in his "14 Points" listed below.

Deming's 14 points: (p. 670)

1. Create constancy of purpose for improvement of product and service.
2. Adopt the new philosophy.
3. Cease dependence on inspection to achieve quality.
4. End business of awarding business on the basis of price tag alone. Instead minimize total cost by working with a single supplier.
5. Improve constantly every process for planning, production and service.
6. Institute training on the job.
7. Adopt and institute leadership.
8. Drive out fear.
9. Break down barriers between departments.
10. Eliminate slogans, exhortations and targets for the workforce.
11. Eliminate numerical quotas for the workforce and numerical goals for the management.
12. Remove barriers that rob people of pride and joy of workmanship and eliminate the annual merit rating system.
13. Institute a vigorous program of education and self-improvement for everyone.
14. Put everyone in the company to work to accomplish the transformation.

Shewhart cycle: a continuous cycle of "plan, do, study and act". **Planning** represents the initial design phase for changing the manufacturing or service process. **Doing** involves carrying out the change, possibly on a small scale. **Studying** consists of analysis of the results using statistical tools that enables the firm to determine what was learned. **Acting** includes either the acceptance of the change and implementation under different conditions or its abandonment. (p. 671)

attribute chart: is used when sampled items are classified according to whether they conform or do not conform to operationally defined requirements. It usually requires nominal or ordinal level of measurement. (p. 674)

p chart: is designed for qualitative variables possessing an attribute that can be classified into one of two mutually exclusive categories, i.e. defective or nondefective. It is used to monitor the proportion of nonconforming items. (p. 674) The control limits are given by the following formula:

$$\overline{p} \pm 3\sqrt{\frac{\overline{p}(1-\overline{p})}{\overline{n}}} \qquad\qquad \overline{p} = \frac{\sum_{i=1}^{k} X_i}{\sum_{i=1}^{n} n_i}$$

where

X_i = number of successes (nonconforming units) in subgroup i;

n_i = number of observations in subgroup i

k = number of subgroups and $\overline{n}$ = average subgroup size

np chart: is also designed for qualitative variables possessing an attribute that can be classified to one of two mutually exclusive categories. (p. 678)

It monitors the number of nonconforming items and calculates the control limits using the normal approximation to the binomial with the following equation:

$$\overline{X} \pm 3\sqrt{\frac{\overline{X}(1-\overline{p})}{q}}$$

244

c chart: is another "attribute" control limit procedure. It monitors the number of nonconformities per unit. (p. 687)

This situation fits the assumptions of the Poisson distribution. The control limits are calculated using the normal approximation of the Poisson distribution with the following formula:

$$\overline{c} \pm 3\sqrt{c}$$

where $\overline{c}$ is the average number of defectives calculated with the following

formula: $\overline{c} = \dfrac{\sum\limits_{i=1}^{k} c_i}{k}$

k is the number of units sampled;

c_i is the number of nonconformities in unit i;

variable control chart: characteristic of interest is measured on an interval or ratio scale. It explains process data both in terms of its variation and in terms of its average. (p. 692)

R chart: used in conjunction with an $\overline{X}$ chart to monitor the variability of the process. (p. 693)

The control limits for the R chart are given by the following formula:

$$\overline{R} \pm \dfrac{3 d_3 \overline{R}}{d_2}$$

where d_3 is a factor which is a function of the sample size and represents the relationship between the standard deviation and the standard deviation of the range.

$\overline{X}$ **chart:** is a control chart that attempts to detect a shift in the process mean. (p.696) The control limits for this and other similar charts are usually set ± three standard deviations around the overall process mean ($\overline{\overline{X}}$). The control limits for the $\overline{X}$ chart are given by the following equation.

$$\overline{\overline{X}} \pm \frac{3\overline{R}}{d_2\sqrt{n}}$$

$$\overline{\overline{X}} = \frac{\sum_{i=1}^{k} \overline{X}_i}{k} \quad and \quad \overline{R} = \frac{\sum_{i=1}^{k} R_i}{k}$$

where $\overline{X}_i$ = the sample mean of n observations at time i;

k = the number of subgroups.

R_i = the range of n observations at time i;

the moving range (MR): the difference between the largest and smallest observations in a subset of n observations over a specified interval of time. (p. 701)

average moving range: is given by the following equation. (p. 701)

$$\overline{MR} = \frac{\sum_{i=1}^{k-1} MR_i}{k-1}$$

where k is the number of observations.

individual value control chart: sets upper and lower control limits to determine the potential existence of special causes of variation for individual values. (p. 702)

control limits for the individual values: is determined using the following equation. (p. 702)

$$\overline{X} \pm \frac{3\overline{MR}}{d_2}$$

where d_2 is a constant factor which is a function of the sample size. It represents the relationship between the standard deviation and range for varying sample sizes. It is obtained from Table E.13.

REVIEW QUESTIONS

1. Classify all of the control chart procedures discussed in the chapter as either "quantitative variable charts" that require actual numerical measurements or "attribute charts" that require categorization of the data.

2. What are the two major causes affecting variability of the product quality? Explain the difference between them.

3. Who is W. E. Deming? Briefly explain his major contributions.

4. Describe **process flow** and **cause and effect** diagrams.

MULTIPLE CHOICE AND FILL IN QUESTIONS

1. The _____ chart monitors the variability of a quality control process.

a) $\overline{X}$ b) c   c) p   d) np   e) R

2. Which one of the following distributions used to determine the control limits for the c chart?

a) normal distribution

b) normal approximation of the binomial

c) binomial

d) normal approximation of the Poisson

3. As the control limits for a process get further apart from each other, the potential quality of the product

a) decreases.   b) increases.

4. For an R chart, the lower control limit is _____ less than zero.

a) always   b) never   c) sometimes

5. The control limits for the c chart are based on the binomial distribution.

a) true   b) false

6. Control charts focus on removing the common causes of variation.

a) true   b) false

7. If a part's measurement falls within the control limits of an $\bar{X}$ chart, then it can be concluded that the part is not defective.

a) true   b) false

8. Even if all of the points fall within the control limits, it is still possible to conclude that the process is out of control.

a) true   b) false

9. Which one of the following charts is based on the binomial distribution?

a) c chart   b) R chart   c) $\bar{X}$ chart   d) p chart

10. The moving range is used in the calculation of the control charts for the

a) process mean.

b) proportion of defectives.

c) individual values.

d) number of defectives per unit.

11. Which one of the following is not considered a special cause of variation?

a) untrained operator

b) poor quality of raw material

c) slight regular machine vibration

d) faulty machine setup

e) worn out tools

12. A "np" chart plots what type of data?

a) nonconforming units per batch

b) nonconformities per unit

c) proportion of nonconforming units per sample

d) nonconforming units per sample

13. A "p" chart plots what type of data?

a) nonconforming units per batch

b) nonconformities per unit

c) proportion of nonconforming units per sample

d) nonconforming units per sample

14. Which one of the following is not an "attribute" chart?

a) $\overline{X}$　　　　b) p　　　　c) np　　　　d) c

15. For a c chart, if an observation falls either below the lower control limit or above the upper control limit, then it can be concluded that the particular observation has an unusually high number of nonconformities per unit.

a) true　　　　　　　b) false

16. Which one of the following is not advocated by Dr. Deming?

a) Break down barriers between departments.

b) Advocate a constant improvement process in products and services.

c) Eliminate slogans.

d) Advocate a strong performance appraisal process based on merit.

e) Advocate a strong staff education and self-improvement program.

EXERCISES

1. Over the last 20 days, daily samples of 50 units of a plastic product were tested for breaking strength. In the twenty samples 40 units failed to conform to the manufacturer's specifications.

a) Determine the control limits for the proportion of defective units per sample.

b) Determine the control limits for the number of defective units per sample.

2. It is desired to control the quality of a process manufacturing small bags of salted peanuts. The quality control manager is concerned about the variability of the weights. The weights of the bags are measured in ounces and the data from six samples are given below. (Note that six samples are not sufficient to determine the control limits for a real world problem. The intention here is to make the manual computations less cumbersome.)

Weight (ounces per bag)					
sample 1	sample 2	sample 3	sample 4	sample 5	sample 6
2.8	2.8	2.0	2.2	2.1	2.4
2.8	2.7	2.2	2.5	2.4	2.5
2.3	2.8	2.3	2.6	2.0	2.8
2.9	2.5	2.1	2.7	2.2	2.7

a) Determine the control limits for the average weight of a bag of peanuts.

b) Determine the control limits for the variability of the process using range as a measure of dispersion.

3. A Pottery company is trying to control the quality of salad bowls. Twenty bowls are selected for this purpose and the number of air bubbles per bowl are counted. These counts are given below:

4, 1, 2, 2, 0, 1, 7, 4, 4, 1, 8, 2, 2, 2, 7, 1, 0, 3, 2, 3.

Set up a control chart for the number of air bubbles per unit. What conclusions can you draw about the process?

4. A manufacturer of light bulbs is trying to control the quality of its products. The quality control personnel randomly select 200 light bulbs from a given shift and classify them as either operational or defective. The following are the number of defective bulbs found in the inspection of 25 shifts (samples) of 200 bulbs per sample:

3, 2, 6, 2, 4, 5, 1, 0, 5, 9, 4, 0, 14, 6, 7, 5, 3, 2, 3, 4, 3, 5, 1, 4, 2.

a) Set up a control chart for the proportion of defectives per sample and indicate whether the process is in control during this period.

b) Set up a control chart for the number of defective units per sample and indicate whether the process is in statistical control during this period.

c) Compare the results obtained from part **a** with the results obtained from part **b**.

5. The state of Ohio Highway Department is studying the amount of traffic at the Indiana border toll gates. Analysts randomly counted the number of cars going through the gates in the eastward direction during a five minute interval. The results of the number of cars going through the gates from twenty consecutive five-minute intervals are given below:

85, 67, 43, 70, 52, 96, 78, 83, 49, 75, 91, 57, 83, 71, 66, 74, 59, 47, 65, 76.

Set up an individual value control chart for this data set. Is the number of cars going through the toll gates in a five minute interval in control?

6. In the manufacturing of tennis balls, the circumference of a ball is a critical factor that must be controlled. Twenty samples of seven balls each resulted in $\bar{\bar{X}}$ = 3.1 inches and $\bar{R}$ = 0.1 inch.

a) Determine the control limits for an $\bar{X}$ and R chart for this process.

b) An operator is in the process of gathering data for the $\bar{X}$ chart. So far, he has gathered six samples of seven balls each which gave him the following sample means: 3.06, 3.11, 3.15, 3.09, 3.07, 3.12 Are any of the sample means outside the control limits. If so, what should the operator do?

ANSWERS TO REVIEW QUESTIONS

1. $\bar{x}$ and R charts require quantitative data, while c, np, and p charts use qualitative data (categorization as conforming vs. nonconforming) as their inputs.

2. The two major causes affecting the variability of output are common causes and special causes. A special cause of variation is due to an assignable individual fluctuation that can be detected and corrected by the workers on the shop floor.

   A common cause of variation is due to the inherent variability in a system of operation. The common causes of variation cannot be controlled by the shop floor personnel. The common causes of variation can only be reduced by changing certain elements of the system which normally requires management action.

3. W. Edward Deming is an internationally famous management consultant/statistician in the area of total quality management whose contributions resulted in major improvements in quality and productivity in many firms in Japan and the United States. He is recognized for successfully applying many of the statistical quality control techniques and developing the theory of "management by process". General Motors, Ford Motor Company and many others are using his methods and ideas to continuously improve their processes. In Japan, the coveted Deming prize is awarded annually to companies that have made the most significant improvement in quality.

4. **The fishbone diagram** is a structured pre-statistical problem solving technique developed by **Kaoru Ishikawa**. It is also known as the Ishikawa diagram. It is used to organize information about the possible reasons and causes of a problem. It attempts to isolate the most probable cause(s) of a problem by category and tries to establish a cause and effect relationship. The basic idea is that once the major cause of the problem is identified, it is easier to solve.

   The process flow diagram depicts the major steps in a process from the beginning to the end. This diagram assists the company in developing a better understanding of the process.

ANSWERS TO MULTIPLE CHOICE AND FILL IN

1. e	9. d
2. d	10. c
3. a	11. c
4. b	12. d
5. b	13. c
6. b	14. a
7. b*	15. b
8. a	16. d

* a part may be within the control limits but outside the specification limits.

SOLUTIONS TO EXERCISES

1. a)

$$\bar{p} = \frac{40}{(20)(50)} = \frac{40}{1000} = .04$$

$$control\ limits = \bar{p} \pm 3\sqrt{\frac{\bar{p}(1-\bar{p})}{\bar{n}}}$$

$$= .04 \pm 3\sqrt{\frac{(.04)(.96)}{50}}$$

$$= .04 \pm 3(.0277)$$

Therefore, LCL = .04 - .083139 = 0

The lower control limit is set to zero because we can not have a negative proportion of defective units.

UCL = .04 + .083139 = .123

b) $\bar{X} = \frac{40}{20} = 2$

$$control\ limits = \bar{X} \pm 3\sqrt{\frac{\bar{X}(1-\bar{p})}{n}}$$

$$= 2 \pm 3\sqrt{2(1-.04)}$$

$$= 2 \pm 4.1569$$

LCL = 0 (impossible to have a negative value)   UCL = 6.1569.

2. $\bar{X}_1 = (2.8 + 2.8 + 2.3 + 2.9)/4 = 2.7$

   $\bar{X}_2 = (2.8 + 2.7 + 2.8 + 2.5)/4 = 2.7$

The other sample means are calculated in a similar fashion and the results for the remaining samples are given below:

$\bar{X}_3 = 2.15$ $\bar{X}_4 = 2.5$ $\bar{X}_5 = 2.175$ $\bar{X}_6 = 2.6$

$$\bar{\bar{X}} = \frac{2.7 + 2.7 + 2.15 + 2.5 + 2.175 + 2.6}{6} = 2.4708$$

The sample range is determined by taking the difference between the largest and the smallest observation in each sample.

$R_1 = 2.9 - 2.3 = .6$ $R_2 = 2.8 - 2.5 = .3$ $R_3 = 2.3 - 2.0 = .3$

$R_4 = 2.7 - 2.2 = .5$ $R_5 = 2.4 - 2.0 = .4$ $R_6 = 2.8 - 2.4 = .4$

$\bar{R} = (.6 + .3 + .3 + .5 + .4 + .4)/6 = .4166$

$$control\ limits = \bar{\bar{X}} \pm \frac{3\bar{R}}{d_2\sqrt{n}}$$

$$= 2.4708 \pm \frac{3(.4166)}{2.059\sqrt{4}}$$

$$= 2.4708 \pm .3035$$

$d_2 = 2.059$ (table E.13)   UCL = 2.7743   LCL = 2.1673

b)

$$\bar{R} \pm \frac{3d_3\bar{R}}{d_2} = .4166 \pm \frac{3(.880)(.4166)}{2.059}$$

$d_3 = .880$ (sample size of four - table E.13)

control limits = .4166 ± .534. LCL =0, UCL =.9507.

3.

$$\bar{c} = \frac{4+1+2+2+0+1+\ldots\ldots+2+3}{20} = \frac{56}{20} = 2.8$$

$$control\ limits = \bar{c} \pm 3\sqrt{(c)}$$
$$control\ limits = 2.8 \pm 3\sqrt{2.8}$$
$$= 2.8 \pm 5.019$$

LCL = 0   UCL = 7.819

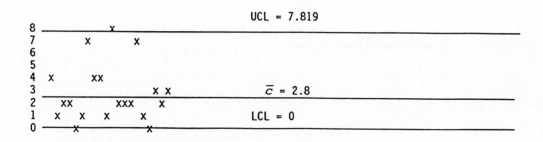

It appears that the number of air bubbles per bowl is not in a state of statistical control because the bowl with 8 air bubbles is outside the upper control limit. Thus the production manager should immediately investigate the process related to the production of that bowl and try to identify the special causes that may have contributed to its nonconformity.

4.

$$\overline{p} = \frac{3+2+6+2+\ldots\ldots+1+4+2}{(200)(25)} = \frac{100}{(200)(25)} = .02$$

$$control\ limits = \overline{p} \pm 3\sqrt{\frac{\overline{p}(1-\overline{p})}{\overline{n}}}$$

$$control\ limits = .02 \pm 3\sqrt{\frac{(.02)(.98)}{200}}$$

$$= .02 \pm .0297$$

LCL = 0 UCL = .0497

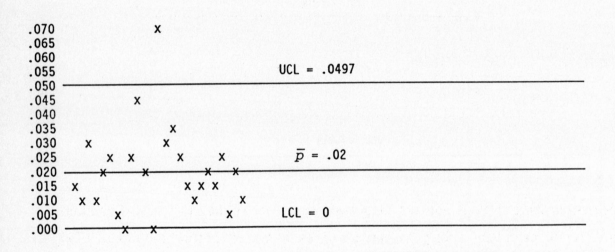

It appears that the process is not in control because for one of the samples, the proportion of defectives exceeds the upper control limit $(14/200) = .07 > .0497$

b)

$$\overline{X} = \frac{100}{25} = 4$$

$$control\ limits = \overline{X} \pm 3\sqrt{\frac{\overline{X}(1-\overline{p})}{n}}$$

$$= 4 \pm 3\sqrt{4(1-.02)}$$

$$= 4 \pm 5.939$$

LCL = 0   UCL = 9.939

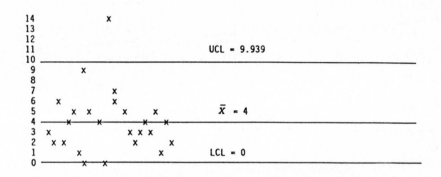

It appears that the process is not in control because for one of the samples, the number of defective (nonconforming) units per sample exceeds the upper control limit (14 > 9.939).

c) The results obtained from the p chart and the np chart are the same.

5.

$$\overline{X} = \frac{85+67+\ldots+65+76}{20} = \frac{1387}{20} = 69.35$$

Sample	Moving range	Sample	Moving range
1	$|85 - 67| = 18$	7	$|78 - 83| = 5$
2	$|67 - 43| = 24$	8	$|83 - 49| = 34$
3	$|43 - 70| = 27$	9	$|49 - 75| = 26$
4	$|70 - 52| = 18$	10	$|75 - 91| = 16$
5	$|52 - 96| = 44$	11	$|91 - 57| = 34$
6	$|96 - 78| = 18$	12	$|57 - 83| = 26$
13	$|83 - 71| = 12$	17	$|59 - 47| = 12$
14	$|71 - 66| = 5$	18	$|47 - 65| = 18$
15	$|66 - 74| = 8$	19	$|65 - 76| = 11$
16	$|74 - 59| = 15$		

$$\overline{MR} = \frac{371}{19} = 19.53$$

For n = 2, d_2 = 1.128 (table E.13)

$$control\ limits = \overline{X} \pm \frac{3\overline{MR}}{d_2}$$

$$control\ limits = 69.35 \pm \frac{3(19.53)}{1.128}$$

$$= 69.35 \pm 51.941$$

LCL = 17.409   UCL = 121.29

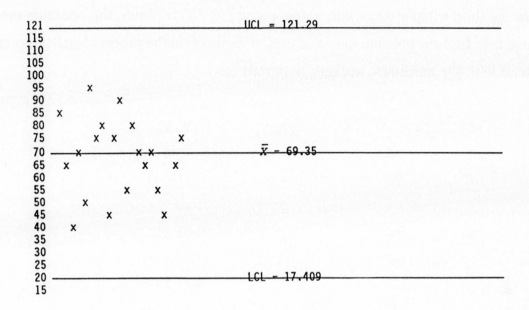

Since none of the observations fall outside the control limits and there is no indication of a series of points above or below the centerline and no indication of a series of consecutive points that are increasing or decreasing, the individual value control chart appears to be within control.

6.

a) d_2 = 2.704 (table E.13)

$$control\ limits = \bar{\bar{X}} \pm \frac{3\bar{R}}{d_2\sqrt{n}}$$

$$= 3.1 \pm \frac{3(.1)}{2.704\sqrt{7}}$$

$$= 3.1 \pm .042$$

LCL = 3.058   UCL = 3.142

$$\bar{R} \pm \frac{3d_3\bar{R}}{d_2} = .1 \pm \frac{3(.833)(.1)}{2.704}$$

$$= .1 \pm .0924$$

where d_3 = .833 (obtained from Table E.13 for n = 7)

LCL = .0076   UCL = .1924

b) Since the third sample mean falls above the upper control limit, the operator should investigate to find any possible special causes of variation in the process (such as potential problems with the machines, workers, materials etc.)

CHAPTER 17

Simple Linear Regression And Correlation

CHAPTER SUMMARY

Throughout most of the text, variables have been described, graphed and analyzed by themselves, without consideration of any possible relationship to other variables. Chapter 13 introduced the concept of relationships between categorical variables with the chi-square test of independence. The relationship between two numerical variables is presented in this chapter.

This chapter discusses two topics; correlation, the association between two variables, and regression, the ability to predict one variable from another due to correlation. Several types of regression models are covered, but the emphasis is on simple linear regression. The assumptions and diagnostics of regression analysis are also addressed.

While the simple regression model pertains to only two variables, the next chapter covers multiple regression, the analysis of the relationships between one dependent variable and a set of independent variables.

KEY CONCEPTS AND TERMS

scatter diagram: a two-dimensional graph used in regression analysis in which the individual values of one independent and one dependent variable are plotted at particular X and Y coordinates. (p. 715)

linear model: straight-line relationship represented as

$$Y_i = \beta_0 + \beta_1 X_i + \epsilon_i \qquad population$$

$$\hat{Y}_i = b_0 + b_1 X_i \qquad sample$$

(p. 719)

least squares method: a mathematical technique that determines the values of b_0 and b_1 that best fit the observed data. Least squares refers to the minimization of the squared

266

differences between actual and predicted values of Y_i. (p. 721)

$$\sum_{i=1}^{n} (Y_i - \hat{Y}_i)^2$$

least-squares equations to determine b_0 and b_1: (p. 722)

$$b_1 = \frac{\sum_{i=1}^{n} X_i Y_i - n\overline{XY}}{\sum_{i=1}^{n} X_i^2 - n\overline{X}^2}$$

$$b_0 = \overline{Y} - b_1\overline{X} \quad where \quad \overline{Y} = \frac{\sum_{i=1}^{n} Y_i}{n} \quad and \quad \overline{X} = \frac{\sum_{i=1}^{n} X_i}{n}$$

standard error of the estimate: the measure of variability around the line of regression. (p. 726)

$$S_{YX} = \sqrt{\frac{\sum_{i=1}^{n} (Y_i - \hat{Y}_i)^2}{n - 2}} = \sqrt{\frac{\sum_{i=1}^{n} Y_i^2 - b_0\sum_{i=1}^{n} Y_i - b_1\sum_{i=1}^{n} X_i Y_i}{n - 2}}$$

where Y_i = actual value of Y for a given X_i

$\hat{Y}_i$ = predicted value of Y for a given X_i

total sum of squares (SST): is a measure of variation of the Y_i values around their mean, $\overline{Y}$. (p. 728)

$$SST = \sum_{i=1}^{n} (Y_i - \overline{Y})^2 = \sum_{i=1}^{n} Y_i^2 - n\overline{Y}^2$$

sum of squares due to regression (SSR): explained variation attributable to the relationship between X and Y. (p. 728)

error sum of squares (SSE): unexplained variation attributable to factors other than the relationship between X and Y. (p. 728)

$$SSR = \sum_{i=1}^{n} (\hat{Y}_i - \overline{Y})^2 = b_0 \sum_{i=1}^{n} Y_i + b_1 \sum_{i=1}^{n} X_i Y_i - n\overline{Y}^2$$

$$SSE = \sum_{i=1}^{n} (Y_i - \hat{Y}_i)^2 = \sum_{i=1}^{n} Y_i^2 - b_0 \sum_{i=1}^{n} Y_i - b_1 \sum_{i=1}^{n} X_i Y_i$$

SST = SSR + SSE: total sum of squares equals sum of squares due to regression plus error sum of squares. (p. 729)

coefficient of determination (r^2): r^2 = SSR/SST and measures the proportion of variation in Y that is explained by the independent variable in the regression model. (p. 731)

adjusted r^2: r^2 which reflects both the number of predictor or explanatory variables in the model and the sample size. (p. 731) In simple linear regression, the formula for adjusted r^2 may be stated as

$$r_{adj}^2 = 1 - \left[(1 - r^2) \frac{n-1}{n-2} \right]$$

coefficient of correlation (ρ): measures the strength of a relationship between two variables in a population with a range from -1 to +1. (p. 732)

sample coefficient of correlation (r): estimator of ρ (p. 733)

$$r = \sqrt{r^2} = \frac{\sum_{i=1}^{n} X_i Y_i - n\overline{XY}}{\sqrt{\sum_{i=1}^{n} X_i^2 - n\overline{X}^2} \sqrt{\sum_{i=1}^{n} Y_i^2 - n\overline{Y}^2}}$$

assumptions of regression: (p. 736)

1. **Normality** - values of Y are normally distributed at each value of X

2. **homoscedasticity** - variation around the line of regression is constant for all values of X

3. **independence of error** - error ("residual" difference between an observed and a predicted value of Y) should be independent for each value of X

4. **linearity** - states that the relationship among the variables is linear

residual or estimated error values (e_i): the difference between the observed (Y_i) and the predicted ($\hat{Y}_i$) values of the dependent variable for given values X_i. (p. 737)

residual analysis: a graphical approach to evaluating the aptness of the fitted regression model by plotting the residuals against the corresponding X_i values. (p. 737)

standardized residuals: (p. 739)

$$SR_i = \frac{e_i}{S_{YX}\sqrt{1 - h_i}} \qquad\qquad h_i = \frac{1}{n} + \frac{(X_i - \overline{X})^2}{\displaystyle\sum_{i=1}^{n} X_i^2 - n\overline{X}^2}$$

where h_i (hat matrix element) reflects the "influence" of each X_i on the fitted regression model.

autocorrelation: a pattern in residuals. When data are collected over sequential periods of time, a residual at any one point in time may tend to be similar to residuals at adjacent points in time. (p. 742)

Durbin-Watson statistic: (p. 744)

$$D = \frac{\displaystyle\sum_{i=2}^{n} (e_i - e_{i-1})^2}{\displaystyle\sum_{i=1}^{n} e_i^2}$$

where e_i = the residual at time period i

confidence interval estimate for predicting $_{YX}$: (p. 747)

$$\hat{Y}_i \pm t_{n-2} S_{YX} \sqrt{\frac{1}{n} + \frac{(X_i - \overline{X})^2}{\displaystyle\sum_{i=1}^{n} X_i^2 - n\overline{X}^2}}$$

$$\hat{Y}_i \pm t_{n-2} S_{YX} \sqrt{1 + \frac{1}{n} + \frac{(X_i - \overline{X})^2}{\sum_{i=1}^{n} X_i^2 - n\overline{X}^2}}$$

test statistic for population parameters: (p. 751)

$$t_{n-2} = \frac{b_1 - \beta_1}{S_{b_1}} \qquad where \ S_{b_1} = \frac{S_{YX}}{\sqrt{\sum_{i=1}^{n} X_i^2 - n\overline{X}^2}}$$

confidence interval of b_1: is a method for testing the existence of a linear relationship between the variables X and Y ($\beta_1 = 0$). (p. 753) It is given by the following formula:

$$b_1 \pm t_{n-2} S_{b_1}$$

test statistic for determining existence of correlation:
The population parameter is hypothesized to be equal to zero;
H_0: $\rho = 0$ (no correlation). (p. 753)

$$t_{n-2} = \frac{r}{\sqrt{\frac{1 - r^2}{n - 2}}}$$

Studentized deleted residual t^*_i: (p. 757)

$$t^*_i = \frac{e_{(i)}}{S_{(i)}\sqrt{1 - h_i}}$$

where $e_{(i)}$ = the difference between the observed Y_i and $\hat{Y}_i$ based on a model that includes all observations except observation i

$S_{(i)}$ = the standard error of the estimate for a model that includes all observations except observation i

Cook's distance statistic, D_i: used to decide if a flagged point is unduly affecting the model. (p. 758)

$$D_i = \frac{SR_i^2 h_i}{2(1 - h_i)}$$

REVIEW QUESTIONS

1. In the linear regression model, what do β_0 and β_1 represent?

2. Least squares is a mathematical minimization technique. What does "least squares" refer to?

3. Why is it important to use only the relevant range of the independent variable in making predictions?

4. In a simple linear model if the value of b_1 is -2.1, how could you describe r?

5. Describe the confidence-band effect for predictions of Y and its interval estimate.

6. Why are the confidence interval formulas different depending upon prediction of average value or individual value?

7. If β_1 is not significantly different from zero, there is no relationship between the dependent and independent variables. Explain.

8. Why is it important to analyze residuals?

9. How can the assumption of independence by evaluated?

10. What is the purpose of the Durbin-Watson statistic and when should it be used?

MULTIPLE CHOICE AND FILL IN QUESTIONS

1. The standard deviation is to the mean as the _____ is to the line of regression.

a) least squares

b) correlation

c) standard error of the estimate

d) influence analysis

e) residual

2. Correlation implies causation.

a) true

b) false

3. The coefficient of determination measures the proportion of _____ that is explained by the _____ variable in the regression model.

4. While the range for r is {-1 ≤ r ≤ +1}, the range for r^2 is _____.

5. The assumption that requires that all variation around the line of regression be constant is called _____.

6. Which of the following is not a major assumption of the regression model?
a) independence of error
b) nominal data
c) normality
d) homoscedasticity

7. The evaluation of the fitted model to determine the potential effect of each particular point on that model is called _____.

8. The least squares regression line minimizes the
a) sum of the differences between actual and predicted Y values.
b) sum of the absolute deviations between actual and predicted Y values.
c) sum of the squared differences between actual and predicted Y values.
d) sum of the absolute deviations between actual and predicted X values.
e) sum of the squared differences between actual and predicted X values.

9. Critical values of the Durbin-Watson statistic are based on _____ and _____.

EXERCISES

To evaluate the relationship of height and weight, the following data was collected from a random sample of 20 students enrolled in an introductory business statistics class.

	Height (inches)	Weight (lbs)		Height (inches)	Weight (lbs)
1	68	175	11	74	200
2	67	130	12	74	183
3	63	125	13	68	170
4	64.5	135	14	70	175
5	74	162	15	75	198
6	72	190	16	67	120
7	71	175	17	72	183
8	75	231	18	65	117
9	73	175	19	65	117
10	72	165	20	74	195

Use this data to answer Questions 1 - 14.

The table on the next page is provided to organize your calculations.

Student	Height X	Weight Y	X^2	Y^2	XY
1	68	175			
2	67	130			
3	63	125			
4	64.5	135			
5	74	162			
6	72	190			
7	71	175			
8	75	231			
9	73	175			
10	72	165			
11	74	200			
12	74	183			
13	68	170			
14	70	175			
15	75	198			
16	67	120			
17	72	183			
18	65	117			
19	65	117			
20	74	195			
Totals					

1. Construct a scatter plot for this data and interpret the plot. The dependent variable is weight and the independent variable is height.

2. Compute the values for b_0 and for b_1 using the least-squares method.

3. What is the sample regression equation? Interpret the meaning of the slope b_1.

4. Compute the standard error of the estimate.

5. Compute the coefficient of determination, r^2 and interpret its meaning in this problem.

6. Using the answer obtained in problem 6 compute the coefficient of correlation, r. Confirm your answer by using Pearson's formula.

7. Compute the adjusted r^2 and compare it with the coefficient of determination r^2.

8. At the .05 level of significance, is there evidence of a linear relationship between height and weight?

9. Determine the 95% confidence-interval estimate for the true slope.

10. Set up a 95% confidence-interval estimate of the average weight of all students who are 70 inches tall.

11. Set up a 95% confidence prediction interval for the weight of a student who is 70 inches tall.

12. Perform a residual analysis on your results and determine the adequacy of the fit of the model. Use the table on the following page to organize your analysis.

Student	Height X	Observed Weight Y	Predicted	Residual	SR$_i$
1	68	175			
2	67	130			
3	63	125			
4	64.5	135			
5	74	162			
6	72	190			
7	71	175			
8	75	231			
9	73	175			
10	72	165			
11	74	200			
12	74	183			
13	68	170			
14	70	175			
15	75	198			
16	67	120			
17	72	183			
18	65	117			
19	65	117			
20	74	195			

13. Compare h_i, t^*_i and D_i for the fifth observation. Do all indicators of influence agree? Rerunning the regression without the fifth observation changes the equation to $\hat{Y}_i = -364.7314 + 7.588489X_i$ and the standard error of the estimate to $S_{YX} = 14.84455$.

14. Simple regression incorporates only one independent variable into the model. If you could add other variables to improve the fit of the model, what other variables would you want to consider. In other words, what other factors might have an effect on weight?

15. The following data represents the number of elected or appointed officials convicted of offenses involving abuse of public office and the years from 1977 to 1991. The third column represents the predicted number of offenses based on simple regression. Use the accompanying table to calculate the Durbin-Watson statistic to test for autocorrelation of residuals.

YEAR	ACTUAL OFFENSES	PREDICTED OFFENSES
1977	94	40.9
1978	91	87.5
1979	102	134.1
1980	131	180.7
1981	159	227.3
1982	147	273.9
1983	424	320.5
1984	429	367.1
1985	470	413.7
1986	523	460.3
1987	545	506.9
1988	529	553.5
1989	610	600.1
1990	583	646.7
1991	665	693.3

n	Y_i	$\hat{Y}_i$	$e_i = Y_i - \hat{Y}_i$	e_{i-1}	$(e_i - e_{i-1})$	$(e_i - e_{i-1})^2$	e_i^2
1	94	40.9					
2	91	87.5					
3	102	134.1					
4	131	180.7					
5	159	227.3					
6	147	273.9					
7	424	320.5					
8	429	367.1					
9	470	413.7					
10	523	460.3					
11	545	506.9					
12	529	553.5					
13	610	600.1					
14	583	646.7					
15	665	693.3					

ANSWERS TO REVIEW QUESTIONS

1. β_0, the Y intercept, is a constant factor included in the equation and β_1 represents the expected unit change in Y per unit change in X.

2. Least squares is the smallest sum of the squared differences between the actual values of Y_i and the predicted values of Y_i.

3. The fitted model is based on the relevant range of the independent variable. If prediction involves values outside of this range, the assumption must be made that the model holds for those values. This may not be a valid assumption.

4. In simple linear regression r takes the sign of b_1. The sign of r would be negative.

5. The confidence-band effect occurs when the width of the confidence interval increases as X moves farther away from its mean. Predictions of Y for values of X close to $\overline{X}$ will have a narrower interval. This can be seen in the formula for the confidence interval. The numerator of h_i reflects the squared distance from X_i to $\overline{X}$. As this distance becomes greater, h_i increases and, in turn, the confidence interval around the predicted Y becomes wider.

6. The interval is wider in predicting a response to a particular value because there is more variation in individual values than in an average value. The interval for predicting average values has less variation and is narrower.

7. If the slope of the regression line (β_1) is zero, the predicted value of Y will always equal the mean of Y, regardless of the value of X. This will occur when there is no significant correlation, or relationship, between X and Y.

8. The aptness of a fitted model can be evaluated by plotting the standardized residuals. Assumptions of the model can also be evaluated by plotting and analyzing residuals.

9. Plotting the residuals in sequential order will reveal any patterns that occur indicating lack of independence among the data.

10. The Durbin-Watson statistic is used to test for autocorrelation among residuals. This test is necessary when the assumption of independent residuals could be violated, as when data is collected over sequential periods of time.

ANSWERS TO MULTIPLE CHOICE AND FILL IN

1. c

2. b

3. variation, independent

4. $(0 \leq r^2 \leq +1)$

5. homoscedasticity

6. b

7. influence analysis

8. c

9. sample size (n), number of independent variables (p)

SOLUTIONS TO EXERCISES

Student	Height X	Weight Y	X^2	Y^2	XY
1	68	175	4624	30625	11900
2	67	130	4489	16900	8710
3	63	125	3969	15625	7875
4	64.5	135	4160.25	18225	8707.5
5	74	162	5476	26244	11988
6	72	190	5184	36100	13680
7	71	175	5041	30625	12425
8	75	231	5625	53361	17325
9	73	175	5329	30625	12775
10	72	165	5184	27225	11880
11	74	200	5476	40000	14800
12	74	183	5476	33489	13542
13	68	170	4624	28900	11560
14	70	175	4900	30625	12250
15	75	198	5625	39204	14850
16	67	120	4489	14400	8040
17	72	183	5184	33489	13176
18	65	117	4225	13689	7605
19	65	117	4225	13689	7605
20	74	195	5476	38025	14430
Totals	1403.5	3321	98781.25	571065	235123.5

$$\sum X = 1403.5 \quad \sum Y = 3321 \quad \sum X^2 = 98781.25 \quad \sum Y^2 = 571065$$
$$\sum XY = 235123.5$$

1.

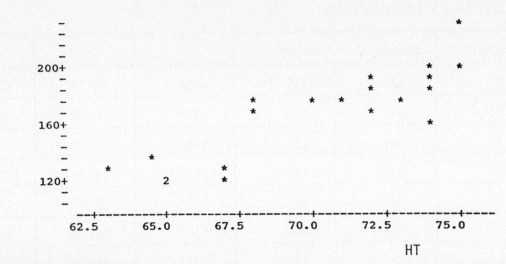

The plot indicates a positive linear relationship. As height increases, weight also increases.

2.

$$b_1 = \frac{\sum\limits_{i=1}^{n} X_i Y_i - n\overline{XY}}{\sum\limits_{i=1}^{n} X_i^2 - n\overline{X}^2}$$

$$= \frac{235123.5 - (20)(70.175)(166.05)}{(98781.25) - (20)(70.175)^2}$$

$$= \frac{2072.325}{290.6375} = 7.130274$$

$$b_0 = \overline{Y} - b_1\overline{X} \quad where \quad \overline{Y} = \frac{\sum\limits_{i=1}^{n} Y_i}{n} \quad and \quad \overline{X} = \frac{\sum\limits_{i=1}^{n} X_i}{n}$$

$$= \frac{(3321)}{20} - (7.130274)\frac{(1403.5)}{20}$$

$$= -334.317$$

3. $\hat{Y}_i = -334.317 + 7.130274X_i$ The meaning of b_1 in this equation is that for every inch of increase in X (height), the value of Y (weight) is expected to increase by 7.130274 lbs.

4.

$$S_{YX} = \sqrt{\frac{\sum_{i=1}^{n} Y_i^2 - b_0 \sum_{i=1}^{n} Y_i - b_1 \sum_{i=1}^{n} X_i Y_i}{n - 2}}$$

$$= \sqrt{\frac{571065 - (-334.317)(3321) - (7.130274)(235123.5)}{18}}$$

$$= 16.392$$

5.

$$SST = \sum_{i=1}^{n} Y_i^2 - n\overline{Y}^2$$

$$SST = 571065 - (20)(166.05)^2 = 19612.95$$

$$SSR = b_0 \sum_{i=1}^{n} Y_i + b_1 \sum_{i=1}^{n} X_i Y_i - n Y^2$$

$$SSR = (334.317)(3321) + (7.130274)(235123.5) - (20)(166.05)^2$$

$$SSR = 14776.15$$

$$SSE = \sum_{i=1}^{n} Y_i^2 - b_0 \sum_{i=1}^{n} Y_i - b_1 \sum_{i=1}^{n} X_i Y_i$$

$$SSE = 571065 - (-334.317)(3321) - (7.130274)(235123.5)$$

$$SSE = 4836.8$$

$$r^2 = \frac{SSR}{SST} = \frac{14776.15}{19612.95}$$

$$r^2 = .7534$$

In this problem, 75.34 percent of the variation in students' weight can be explained by the variation in students' height.

6. Since $r^2 = .7534$, $r = \sqrt{.7534} = .8680$

r can also be obtained by using Pearson's formula:

$$r = \frac{\sum_{i=1}^{n} X_i Y_i - n\overline{XY}}{\sqrt{\sum_{i=1}^{n} X_i^2 - n\overline{X}^2}\sqrt{\sum_{i=1}^{n} Y_i^2 - n\overline{Y}^2}}$$

$$r = \frac{235123.5 - (20)(70.175)(166.05)}{\sqrt{98781.25 - (20)(70.175)^2}\sqrt{571065 - (20)(166.05)^2}}$$

$$r = .8680$$

7.

$$r_{adj}^2 = 1 - \left[(1 - r^2)\frac{n-1}{n-2}\right]$$

$$= 1 - \left[(1 - .7534)\frac{19}{18}\right]$$

$$= .7397$$

The adjusted r^2 is only slightly less than the coefficient of determination (.7397 as compared to .7534).

8. H_0: $\beta = 0$ H_1: $\beta \neq 0$ The critical value of $t_{n-2} = t_{18, .025} = 2.1009$

$$t_{n-2} = \frac{b_1 - \beta_1}{\dfrac{S_{YX}}{\sqrt{\sum_{i=1}^{n} X_i^2 - n\overline{X}^2}}}$$

$$= \frac{7.130274 - 0}{\dfrac{16.39}{\sqrt{98781.25 - (20)(70.175)^2}}}$$

$$= 7.416$$

The test statistic, 7.416, is greater than the critical value of 2.1009 and, therefore, falls in the rejection region. Rejection of the null hypothesis provides evidence of the linear relationship between height and weight.

9.

$$b_1 \pm t_{n-2} \frac{S_{YX}}{\sqrt{\sum_{i=1}^{n} X_i^2 - \frac{\left(\sum_{i=1}^{n} X_i\right)^2}{n}}}$$

$$= 7.130274 \pm 2.1009 \frac{16.39}{\sqrt{98781.25 - \frac{(1403.5)^2}{20}}}$$

$$= 7.130274 \pm 2.0198$$

$P(5.11 \leq \beta_1 \leq 9.15) = .95$

As zero does not fall within this interval, a linear relationship is further supported.

10. $\hat{Y}_i = -334.317 + 7.130274 X_i$ If $X_i = 70$, $\hat{Y}_i = -334.317 + 7.130274\,(70) = 164.8$

$$\hat{Y}_i \pm t_{n-2} S_{YX} \sqrt{\frac{1}{n} + \frac{(X_i - \overline{X})^2}{\sum_{i=1}^{n} X_i^2 - n\overline{X}^2}}$$

$$\overline{X} = \frac{1403.5}{20}$$

$$\overline{X} = 70.175$$

$$164.8 \pm (2.1009)(16.39)\sqrt{\frac{1}{20} + \frac{(70 - 70.175)^2}{98781.25 - (20)(70.175)^2}}$$

$$164.8 \pm 7.708$$

$P(157.092 \leq \mu_{yx} \leq 172.508) = .95$

11.

$$\hat{Y}_i \pm t_{n-2} S_{YX} \sqrt{1 + \frac{1}{n} + \frac{(X_i - \bar{X})^2}{\sum\limits_{i=1}^{n} X_i^2 - n\bar{X}^2}}$$

$$164.8 \pm (2.1009)(16.39) \sqrt{1 + \frac{1}{20} + \frac{(70 - 70.175)^2}{98781.25 - (20)(70.175)^2}}$$

$$164.8 \pm 35.3$$

$$P(129.5 \leq \hat{Y}_i \leq 200.1) = .95$$

12. Based on the type of data, we can test for homoscedasticity and normality using residual analysis. Calculate standardized residuals for all 20 observations using the following example of the first observation. Using a computer in residual analysis is strongly recommended to improve accuracy and efficiency. A completed residual table is on the following page.

$$h_i = \frac{1}{n} + \frac{(X_i - \bar{X})^2}{\sum\limits_{i=1}^{n} X_i^2 - n\bar{X}^2}$$

$$h_1 = \frac{1}{20} + \frac{(68 - 70.175)^2}{98781.25 - (20)(70.175)^2}$$

$$h_1 = .066$$

$$SR_i = \frac{e_i}{S_{YX}\sqrt{1 - h_i}}$$

$$SR_1 = \frac{24.458}{16.39\sqrt{1 - .066}} = 1.54$$

Student	Height X	Observed Weight Y	Predicted	Residual	SR_i
1	68	175	150.542	24.458	1.54
2	67	130	143.411	-13.411	-.86
3	63	125	114.890	10.110	.70
4	64.5	135	125.586	9.414	.63
5	74	162	193.323	-31.323	-2.01
6	72	190	179.063	10.937	.69
7	71	175	171.932	3.068	.19
8	75	231	200.454	30.546	2.00
9	73	175	186.193	-11.193	-.71
10	72	165	179.063	-14.063	-.89
11	74	200	193.323	6.677	.43
12	74	183	193.323	-10.323	-.66
13	68	170	150.542	19.458	1.23
14	70	175	164.802	10.198	.64
15	75	198	200.454	-2.454	-.16
16	67	120	143.411	-23.411	-1.49
17	72	183	179.063	3.937	.25
18	65	117	129.151	-12.151	-.80
19	65	117	129.151	-12.151	-.80
20	74	195	193.323	1.677	.11

To test for homoscedasticity, construct a residual plot with X_i on the X axis and SR_i on the Y axis. This plot will graphically display any patterns or relationships which would violate the assumption of constant variation.

Plotting the standardized residuals on a histogram will allow you to subjectively test the assumption of normality of residuals.

The assumptions of normality and constant variance appear to be supported by the plots of the standardized residuals. No patterns are evident and the shape of the errors approximates a normal distribution. While it is difficult to draw conclusions based on a sample size of only 20, the plots support the assumptions of normality and constant variation.

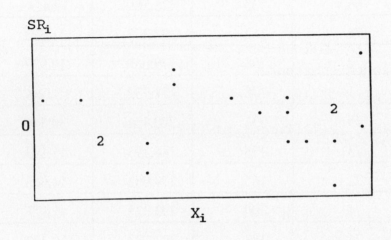

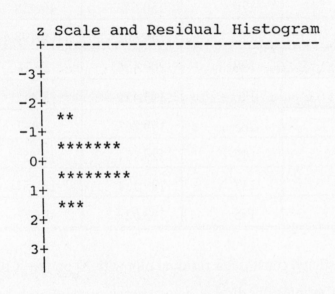

13.

$$h_5 = \frac{1}{n} + \frac{(X_5 - \overline{X})^2}{\sum\limits_{i=1}^{n} X_i^2 - n\overline{X}^2}$$

$$= \frac{1}{20} + \frac{(74 - 70.175)^2}{98781.25 - (20)(70.175)^2}$$

$$= .100$$

The rule of thumb is that if $h_i > 4/n$, X_i is an influential point. $H_5 = .1 < (4/20 = .20)$ and is, therefore not an influential point.

To calculate t^*_5, use the regression equation and standard error of the revised model without observation 5. H_5 remains the same.

$$t_5^* = \frac{e_{(5)}}{S_{(5)}\sqrt{1 - h_i}}$$

$$= \frac{-34.82}{14.84\sqrt{1 - .10}}$$

$$= -2.47$$

The critical value of $t_{.10, \, n-3}$, is $t_{.05,17}$ for a two-tailed test and equals 1.7396. Because $|-2.47| > 1.7396$, t_5 falls in the rejection region and this test indicates that the fifth observation is an influential point that adversely affects the model.

$$D_5 = \frac{SR_5^2 \, h_5}{2(1 - h_5)}$$

$$= \frac{(-2.01)^2(.1)}{2(1 - .1)}$$

$$= .22$$

The rule of thumb is that if $D_i > F_{.5, \, 2, \, n-2}$, the observation may have an impact on the results of fitting the model. The critical value of F for a sample of size 20 is approximately .718 (Table E.5). Because $D_5 = .22 < .718$, D_5 does not fall in the rejection region and is not a candidate for removal.

294

Results from all three tests are not consistent, and, therefore, there is no clear basis for removing the fifth observation from the fitted model.

14. Other variables to be considered might be age, gender or build. Multiple regression, covered in the next chapter, predicts the value of a dependent variable based on several independent, predictor variables.

15.

n	Y_i	$\hat{Y}_i$	$e_i = Y_i - \hat{Y}_i$	e_{i-1}	$(e_i - e_{i-1})$	$(e_i - e_{i-1})^2$	e_i^2
1	94	40.9	53.1	0.0	0.0	0.0	2819.6
2	91	87.5	3.5	53.1	-49.6	2460.2	12.3
3	102	134.1	-32.1	3.5	-35.6	1267.1	1030.4
4	131	180.7	-49.7	-32.1	-17.6	309.8	2470.1
5	159	227.3	-68.3	-49.7	-18.6	346.0	4664.9
6	147	273.9	-126.9	-68.3	-58.6	3434.0	16103.6
7	424	320.5	103.5	-126.9	230.4	53084.2	10712.3
8	429	367.1	61.9	103.5	-41.6	1730.6	3831.6
9	470	413.7	56.3	61.9	-5.6	31.4	3169.7
10	523	460.3	62.7	56.3	6.4	41.0	3931.3
11	545	506.9	38.1	62.7	-24.6	605.2	1451.6
12	529	553.5	-24.5	38.1	-62.6	3918.8	600.2
13	610	600.1	9.9	24.5	-14.6	213.2	98.0
14	583	646.7	-63.7	9.9	-73.6	5417.0	4057.7
15	665	693.3	-28.3	63.7	-92.0	8464.0	800.9
				Totals		81322.0	55754.0

$$D = \frac{\sum_{i=2}^{n}(e_i - e_{i-1})^2}{\sum_{i=1}^{n} e_i^2} = \frac{81322}{55754} = 1.46$$

From the table of critical values, n = 15 and p = 1, d_u = 1.36. As 1.46 > 1.36, there is no evidence of autocorrelation among the residuals.

CHAPTER 18

Multiple Regression Models

CHAPTER SUMMARY

The previous chapter introduced the concept of a linear relationship between two numerical variables. Often the fit of a regression model can be improved by including more than one independent variable, by adding categorical variables or by adding nonlinear variables to the model.

This chapter focuses on model improvement through the incorporation of multiple independent, nonlinear and/or categorical (dummy) variables into the regression model. Logistic regression which uses regression models to predict the probability of categorical responses is also discussed. Techniques are introduced to evaluate the contribution of each variable to the model and to compare models to determine which have the best fit. The problem of multicollinearity is also discussed. An example of model building using stepwise regression is included at the end of the chapter.

KEY CONCEPTS AND TERMS

multiple regression: models in which several explanatory variables can be used to predict the value of a dependent variable. (p. 784)

$$Y_i = \beta_0 + \beta_1 X_{1i} + \beta_2 X_{2i} + \beta_3 X_{3i} + \ldots + \beta_p X_{pi} + \epsilon_i$$

where β_0 = Y intercept

$\quad \beta_1$ = slope of Y with variable X_1 holding variables $X_2, \ldots X_p$ constant

$\quad \beta_p$ = slope of Y with variable X_p holding variables $X_1, \ldots X_{p-1}$ constant

$\quad \epsilon_i$ = random error in Y for observation i

$\quad p$ = number of explanatory variables in the regression model

sample multiple regression equation: (p. 785)

$$\hat{Y}_i = b_0 + b_1 X_{1i} + b_2 X_{2i} + b_3 X_{3i} + \ldots + b_p X_{pi}$$

net regression coefficient: represents the unit change in Y_i per unit change in X_i, taking into account the effect of the remaining X_i. This is represented by β_i. (p. 784)

coefficient of multiple determination (r^2): represents the proportion of the variation in Y that is explained by the set of explanatory variables $r^2_{Y.12} = \frac{SSR}{SST}$. (p. 790)

adjusted r^2: reflects both the number of explanatory variables in the model and the sample size. (p. 791)

$$r^2_{adj} = 1 - \left[(1 - r^2_{Y.12...p}) \frac{n-1}{n-p-1} \right]$$

correlation matrix: a matrix which indicates the coefficient of correlation between each pair of variables. (p. 791)

analysis-of-variance (ANOVA) table for multiple regression: (p. 795)

SOURCE	df	SUMS OF SQUARES	MEAN SQUARE (VARIANCE)	F
Regression	p	SSR	$MSR = \frac{SSR}{p}$	$F = \frac{MSR}{MSE}$
Error	n-p-1	SSE	$MSE = \frac{SSE}{n-p-1}$	
Total	n-1	SST		

error variance: the measure of random error (MSE). (p. 795)

F test: ratio of the variance due to the regression divided by the error variance $F = \frac{MSR}{MSE}$. (p. 795)

partial F test criterion: the contribution to the regression sum of squares made by each explanatory variable after all other explanatory variables have been included in a model. (p. 797)

$$F = \frac{SSR(X_k| \; all \; variables \; except \; k)}{MSE}$$

determining the contribution of an explanatory variable by comparing different regression models using SSR (all variables except k): the regression sum of squares of a model that includes all explanatory variables except of the one of interest. (p. 797)

SSR $(X_k|$ all variables except k) =

SSR (all variables including k) - SSR (all variables except k)

hypothesis test of population parameters: (p. 801)

$$t = \frac{b_k}{S_{b_k}}$$

t and F relationship: $t_a^2 = F_{1,a}$ (p. 803)

where a = number of degrees of freedom

confidence-interval estimation: (p. 803)

$$b_k \pm t_{n-p-1}S_{b_k}$$

coefficient of partial determination: measures the proportion of the variation in the dependent variable that is explained by each explanatory variable while controlling for, or holding constant, the other explanatory variable(s). (p. 805)

$$r^2_{YK.(all\ variables\ except\ k)} = \frac{SSR(X_k|\ all\ variables\ except\ k)}{[SST - SSR(all\ variables\ including\ k) + SSR(X_k|\ all\ variables\ except\ k)]}$$

polynomial relationship: Y increases (or decreases) at a changing rate for various values of X. (p. 806)

$$\hat{Y}_i = b_0 + b_1X_{1i} + b_{11}X_{1i}^2$$

where b_0 = Y intercept

b_1 = linear effect on Y

b_{11} = curvilinear effect on Y

centered regression model: the mean of the explanatory variable is subtracted from each value in the model to increase accuracy and to deflate the variance. (p. 807)

$$\hat{Y}_i = b_0' + b_1'(X_{1i} - \overline{X}_1) + b_{11}(X_{1i} - \overline{X}_1)^2$$

dummy variable: the vehicle that permits the researcher to consider categorical explanatory variables as part of the regression model. (p. 817)

interaction terms: when the relationship between X_1 and Y changes for differing values of X_2, the product of the explanatory variables is included in the model. (p. 821)

$\hat{Y}_i = b_0 + b_1X_{1i} + b_2X_{2i} + b_3X_{1i}X_{2i}$ where b_3 is the slope of the interaction term

transformations: transforming the dependent or independent variable often overcomes the effects of violations of assumptions of the regression model. Common transformations include square-root, logarithmic and reciprocal transformations. (p. 822)

multicollinearity: situations in which some of the explanatory variables are highly correlated with each other. (p. 824)

variance inflationary factor (VIF): measure of collinearity. (p. 824)

$$VIF_j = \frac{1}{1 - R_j^2}$$

where R^2_j equals the coefficient of multiple determination of explanatory variable X_j with all other X variables

stepwise regression: an attempt to find the best regression model without examining all possible regressions. This model building technique adds or deletes variables to the model until no further improvement can be made. (p. 829)

C_{p*} statistic: criterion used in evaluating competing regression models (p. 835)

$$C_{p*} = \frac{(1 - R_{p*}^2)(n - T)}{1 - R_T^2} - (n - 2p^*)$$

where $p^* = p + 1 =$ number of parameters included in a regression model with p independent variables

    T   = total number of parameters to be considered for inclusion in the regression model

    R_{p*}^2 = coefficient of multiple determination for a regression model that has p^* parameters

R_T^2 = coefficient of multiple determination for a regression model that contains all T parameters

logistic regression: regression based on odds ratio which predicts probability of a particular categorical response for a given set of explanatory variables (which could be numerical or categorical). (p. 837)

odds ratio: (p. 837)

$$Odds\ ratio = \frac{probability\ of\ success}{1 - probability\ of\ success}$$

logistic regression model: (p. 838)

$$\ln(Odds\ ratio) = \beta_0 = \beta_1 x_{1i} + \beta_2 x_{2i} + . + \beta_k x_{ki} + \epsilon_i$$

where k = the number of independent variables in the model

ϵ = random error for observation i

estimated probability of success: (p. 838)

$$Estimated\ probability\ of\ success = \frac{estimated\ odds\ ratio}{1 + estimated\ odds\ ratio}$$

deviance statistic: measures the fit of the current model compared to a model that has as many parameters as there are data points (saturated model). (p. 840)

Wald statistic: ratio of the regression coefficient to the standard error of the regression coefficient. (p. 841)

REVIEW QUESTIONS

1. Interpret the meaning of the intercept (b_0) and slope (b_1) in a multiple regression model with two explanatory variables, X_1 and X_2.

2. In determining whether there is a significant relationship between the dependent variable and the set of explanatory variables, what are the hypotheses being tested?

3. Compare the coefficient of determination to the coefficient of multiple determination.

4. Name and explain two methods of determining the contribution of an explanatory variable.

5. Compare the F test ratio to the partial F-test criterion.

6. Explain the relationship of the t statistic and the partial F statistic.

7. Compare the coefficient of partial determination to the coefficient of multiple determination (i.e., $r^2_{Y.12}$ to $r^2_{Y1.2}$).

8. A centered regression model affects which terms?

9. What is the benefit of using stepwise regression in model building?

10. In what situation would you consider using logistic regression?

MULTIPLE CHOICE AND FILL IN QUESTIONS

1. _____ occurs when explanatory variables are highly correlated with each other.

2. A model building technique which takes advantage of the partial F criterion is called _____ _____.

3. In determining significant relationships, testing the curvilinear effect and the linear effect of a curvilinear model is similar to testing all slopes ($b_{1..p}$) in a linear model.

a) true   b) false

4. You wish to add a categorical explanatory variable with two categories to a regression model. How many dummy variables are required to represent the categories?

a) one   b) two

5. In some situations, the use of a transformation can change what appears to be a _____ model into a linear model.

6. When the relationship between X_1 and Y changes for differing values of X_2, a(n) _____ term is required.

7. Due to multiple slopes (b_i), residual plots cannot be constructed for the residual analysis of multiple regression models.

a) true   b) false

8. If a set of explanatory variables are uncorrelated, VIF will be equal to _____.

a) zero   b) -1

c) +1   d) < 1   e) > 1

9. In influence analysis, Cook's D_i , which is based on both _____ and _____, should be used in cases of inconsistent results between h_i and t^*_i.

a) sample size, the number of explanatory variables

b) degrees of freedom, variance

c) the standardized residual, t^*_i

d) h_i, the standardized residual

e) h_i, t^*_i

10. When using logistic regression, the fit of the model can be tested with the _____ statistic and the contribution of each independent variable can be tested with the _____ statistic.

EXERCISES

1. To further evaluate the relationship of height and weight, (where height is used to predict weight in Chapter 17) a second explanatory variable, gender, was added to the simple regression model. The additional data is provided in the table below. Access a computer package and perform multiple linear regression analysis. (Hint: Use a dummy variable for "gender", $X_d = 0$ if male and $X_d = 1$ if female)

	Height inches	Weight (lbs)	Gender M/F		Height inches	Weight (lbs)	Gender M/F
1	68	175	M	11	74	200	M
2	67	130	F	12	74	183	M
3	63	125	F	13	68	170	M
4	64.5	135	F	14	70	175	M
5	74	162	M	15	75	198	M
6	72	190	M	16	67	120	F
7	71	175	M	17	72	183	M
8	75	231	M	18	65	117	F
9	73	175	M	19	65	117	F
10	72	165	M	20	74	195	M

a) State the multiple regression equation.

b) Interpret the meaning of the slopes in the context of this problem.

c) Predict the weight of a 70 inch male.

d) Determine whether there is a significant relationship between weight and the two explanatory variables (height and gender) at the .05 level of significance.

e) What is the p value in part (d) and interpret its meaning.

f) Set up a 95% confidence-interval estimate of the true population slope between weight and height.

g) What is the coefficient of multiple determination $r^2_{Y.12}$ and interpret its meaning.

h) Compute the adjusted r^2 and compare it to the adjusted r^2 of the simple regression model which used only height to predict weight (Chapter 17). Which model (single or multiple regression) explains more of the variation in students' weight?

i) Compute the coefficients of partial determination ($r^2_{Y1.2}$ and $r^2_{Y2.1}$) and interpret their meanings.

j) Is there evidence of multicollinearity in this model? (Hint: use the VIF method)

2. When adding a third independent variable, shoe size, to the data in question 1, the coefficients of multiple determination for each combination of variables was obtained. Use the C_{p*} statistic to evaluate each of the five models.

Height	Weight	Gender	Shoe Size
68.0	175	0	12.0
67.0	130	1	7.0
63.0	125	1	6.5
64.5	135	1	8.5
74.0	162	0	11.0
72.0	190	0	10.0
71.0	175	0	9.0
75.0	231	0	12.0
73.0	175	0	12.0
72.0	165	0	11.0
74.0	200	0	11.5
74.0	183	0	11.0
68.0	170	0	12.5
70.0	175	0	10.5
75.0	198	0	12.5
67.0	120	1	8.0
72.0	183	0	11.0
65.0	117	1	6.0
65.0	117	1	8.0
74.0	195	0	10.0

Model	R^2
H	.753
H/G	.827
H/S	.813
G/S	.781
H/G/S	.834

3. To improve the effectiveness of their advertising, an airline wanted to determine if there was a relationship between annual salary and accumulated annual frequent flyer miles. A random sample of their customer data base provided the following results.

Customer	Salary	Miles
1	$103	120
2	135	53
3	60	65
4	31	16
5	121	92
6	152	10
7	85	130
8	53	40
9	74	93
10	140	34

(Salary and Miles are in thousands)

a) Construct a scatter diagram of salary (X) and miles (Y).

b) State the equation of the curvilinear model using the centered regression model.

c) Determine if there is a significant curvilinear relationship between salary and miles at the .05 level of significance.

d) Determine if there is a significant linear relationship between salary and miles at the .05 level of significance.

4. In a logistic regression analysis with n = 55, p = 3 and α =.05, interpret the meaning of the following:

    a. deviance statistic = 42.34

    b. Wald statistic for X_1 = 2.78

c. Wald statistic for X_2 = 3.20

d. Wald statistic for X_3 = 1.24

ANSWERS TO REVIEW QUESTIONS

1. The Y intercept represents the value of the dependent variable when both explanatory variables are equal to zero ($X_1 = X_2 = 0$). For a given value of X_2, the slope of X_1 (b_1) represents the amount of increase (or decrease) in the dependent variable for every unit change in X_1.

2. The null hypothesis is that there is no linear relationship between the dependent variable and the explanatory variables. The alternative hypothesis is that at least one regression coefficient is not equal to zero. Rejection of H_0 implies that at least one explanatory variable is making a significant reduction in the error variation.

3. The coefficient of determination is the proportion of variation in Y that is explained by X while the coefficient of multiple determination is the proportion of variation in Y that is explained by the set of explanatory variables.

4. By comparing different regression models, the contribution of explanatory variables can be analyzed. The first method of comparing models uses sums of squares. For each explanatory variable a regression sum of squares is computed which includes the effect of all explanatory variables except itself. From these values we can determine the contribution of each variable after the others have been included in the model (the amount of additional contribution unique to that variable). The second method uses the C_{p*} statistic to evaluate alternative models, again analyzing the contribution of explanatory variables included in each model.

5. Both tests are a ratio of variance due to regression divided by the error variance. The regression variance of the F test includes all explanatory variables. The regression

variance of the partial F test is made up only of the additional effect of the explanatory variable of interest, after all others have been included in the model. The general F tests the fit of the overall model and the partial F tests the contribution of individual variables.

6. When F is used to test an individual variable (numerator degrees of freedom equals one and denominator degrees of freedom equals x), its value is equal to the square of t with x degrees of freedom.

7. The coefficient of multiple determination measures the proportion of variation in Y that is explained by all of the explanatory variables. The coefficient of partial determination measures the proportion of variation in Y that is explained by each explanatory variable while controlling for, or holding constant, the other explanatory variable(s).

8. The centered model modifies the intercept (b_0') and the linear effect (b_1').

9. Stepwise regression attempts to find the best model without examining all possible variable combinations.

10. Logistic regression could be used when the response variable is a categorical variable which takes on one of only two values (represented as zero or one). Using least squares regression in this case could lead to a predicted value of less than zero or greater than one, values that cannot possibly occur.

ANSWERS TO MULTIPLE CHOICE AND FILL IN

1. multicollinearity
2. stepwise regression
3. a
4. a
5. nonlinear
6. interaction
7. b
8. c
9. d
10. deviance, Wald

SOLUTIONS TO EXERCISES

1.

SOURCE	df	SUMS OF SQUARES	MEAN SQUARE (VARIANCE)	F
Regression	2	16223.76	8111.881	40.69*
Error	17	3389.188	199.364	
Total	19	19612.95		

* p value = .00000033

Table of Estimated Coefficients

Variable	Parameter Estimate	Standard Error	t	p value
Height	3.59248	1.55233	2.314	.033422
Gender	-34.79575	12.91331	-2.695	.015348
Intercept	-75.61383			

Coefficient of multiple determination = .8272

Standard error of the estimate = 14.12

a) $\hat{Y}_i$ = -75.61383 + 3.59248X_1 - 34.79575X_2

b) The slope of height with weight (b_1 = 3.59248) can be interpreted to mean that for a student of given gender, his/her weight will increase by 3.59248 pounds for every one inch increase in height. The slope of gender with weight (b_2 = - 34.79575) can be interpreted as follows. Since X_2 = 0 is for males and X_2 = 1 for females, for a student with a given height, the weight will be 34.79575 pounds less for a female than for a male.

c) $\hat{Y}_i$ = -75.61383 + 3.59248(70) - 34.79575(0) = 175.86 pounds

d) H_0: β_1 = β_2 = 0 (There is no relationship between weight and height and gender)
H_1: $\beta_1 \neq \beta_2 \neq 0$ (At least one regression coefficient is not equal to zero)
Decision Rule: reject H_0 if $F_{2,17}$ > 3.59. Because 40.69 > 3.59, reject the null hypothesis - at least one of the variables of height or gender is related to weight.

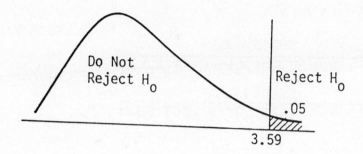

e) The p value = .00000033 < α = .05, which again supports rejection of the null hypothesis of no relationship.

f) The 95% estimate of the true population slope is

$$b_1 \pm t_{n-p-1} S_{b_1}$$

3.592484 ± (2.1098)(1.552338)

3.592484 ± 3.275

.317484 ≤ β_1 ≤ 6.867

g) The coefficient of multiple determination, $r^2_{Y.12}$, is .8272 which means that 82.72% of the variation in weight is explained by height and gender.

h)

$$r^2_{adj} = 1 - \left[(1 - r^2_{Y.12}) \frac{n - 1}{n - p - 1} \right]$$

$$= 1 - \left[(1 - .8272) \frac{20 - 1}{20 - 2 - 1} \right]$$

$$= .8069$$

Adjusted r^2 from the simple regression model was .7397 compared to .8069 from the multiple regression model. The multiple regression model explains a greater percentage of variation in weight.

i)

$$r^2_{Y1.2)} = \frac{SSR(X_1 \mid X_2)}{SST - SSR(X_1 \text{ and } X_2) + SSR(X_1 \mid X_2)}$$

$$= \frac{1067.7335}{19612.95 - 16223.76 + 1067.7335}$$

$$= .2396$$

$$r^2_{Y2.1)} = \frac{SSR(X_2 \mid X_1)}{SST - SSR(X_1 \text{ and } X_2) + SSR(X_2 \mid X_1)}$$

$$= \frac{1447.5181}{19612.95 - 16223.76 + 1447.5181}$$

$$= .2993$$

The coefficient of partial determination of weight with height, while holding gender constant, can be interpreted to mean that for a fixed (constant) gender, 23.96% of the variation in weight can be explained by the variation in height.

j)   <u>Matrix of Correlation Coefficients</u>

	Weight	Height	Gender
Weight	1.0000	.8680	-.8791
Height	.8680	1.0000	-.8458
Gender	-.8791	-.8458	1.0000

$$VIF_1 = \frac{1}{1 - R_1^2} = \frac{1}{1 - (-.8458)^2} = 3.5$$

As the variance inflationary factor is less than the most conservative lower bound of 5, it would appear that multicollinearity is not a problem with this model.

2.

Model	R^2	C_{p*}
H	.753	7.81
H/G	.827	2.67
H/S	.813	4.02
G/S	.781	7.11
H/G/S	.834	4.00

$$C_p.Model H = \frac{(1 - .753)(20 - 4)}{(1 - .834)} - (20 - 4) = 7.81$$

$$C_p.Model H/G = \frac{(1 - .827)(20 - 4)}{(1 - .834)} - (20 - 6) = 2.67$$

$$C_p.Model H/S = \frac{(1 - .813)(20 - 4)}{(1 - .834)} - (20 - 6) = 4.02$$

$$C_p.Model G/S = \frac{(1 - .781)(20 - 4)}{(1 - .834)} - (20 - 6) = 7.11$$

$$C_p.Model H/G/S = \frac{(1 - .834)(20 - 4)}{(1 - .834)} - (20 - 8) = 4.00$$

The model including height and gender to predict weight appears to be the "best" model based on C_{p*}.

3.

a)

MILES

SALARY

b) Based on the mean of X ($\bar{x}$) = 95.4, the following table was developed:

X	(X-$\bar{x}$)	(X-$\bar{x}$)^2
103	7.6	57.76
135	39.6	1568.16
60	-35.4	1253.16
31	-64.4	4147.36
121	25.6	655.36
152	56.6	3203.56
85	-10.4	108.16
53	-42.4	1797.76
74	-21.4	457.96
140	44.6	1989.16

The regression was run with the centered values and the equation is $\hat{Y}_i$ = 110.3458 - .155989(X-$\bar{x}$) -.029561(X -$\bar{x}$)^2

TABLE OF ESTIMATED COEFFICIENTS

```
=================================================
                Estimated      Estimated    Computed
Variable        Coefficient    St. Dev.     t-Value
-------------------------------------------------
X               -0.155989      0.134816     -1.157
X2              -0.029561      0.004146     -7.130
Intercept       110.3458
-------------------------------------------------
```

c) To test the curvilinear relationship, H_0: $\beta_{11} = 0$, H_1: $\beta_{11} \neq 0$

$$t_{n-3} = \frac{b_{11}}{S_{b_{11}}}$$

$$= \frac{-.029561}{.004146} = -7.130$$

$|-7.13|$ is larger than the critical value ($t_7 = 2.3646$) and the null hypothesis is rejected. Including the curvilinear effect significantly improves the model.

d) To test the linear relationship, H_0: $\beta_1' = 0$, H_1: $\beta_1' \neq 0$

$$t_{n-3} = \frac{b_1'}{S_{b_1'}}$$

$$= \frac{-.155989}{.134816} = -1.157$$

$|-1.157|$ is smaller than the critical value ($t_7 = 2.3646$) and the null hypothesis is not rejected. Including the linear effect does not significantly improve the model.

4.

a. The critical value for the deviance statistic with $\alpha = .05$ is $\chi^2_{(55-3-1)} = 68.669$ which is larger than 42.34. Therefore the H_0 is not rejected and we would conclude that the model is a good fit.

b. The critical value for the Wald test using $\alpha = .05$ is 1.96. The Wald statistic for X_1 is greater than 1.96 ($2.78 > 1.96$) indicating that X_1 makes a contribution to the model.

c. The critical value for the Wald test using $\alpha = .05$ is 1.96. The Wald statistic for X_2 is greater than 1.96 ($3.20 > 1.96$) indicating that X_2 makes a contribution to the model.

d. The critical value for the Wald test using $\alpha = .05$ is 1.96. The Wald statistic for X_3 is less than 1.96 ($1.24 < 1.96$) indicating that X_3 does not make a contribution to the model.

NOTES

CHAPTER 19
Time-Series Forecasting

CHAPTER SUMMARY

Forecasting has a prime importance in any business organization because it forms the basis for making long term management decisions in all areas of business. The areas of a business that use forecasts to make decisions include but are not limited to the following: production planning, inventory management, work force and sales force planning, capital investment management, capacity planning and budgeting. There are many ways of obtaining forecasts. This chapter provides a discussion of some of these forecasting procedures. The majority of discussion emphasizes the use of time series in forecasting, where knowledge of the past is used to predict the future. In addition to the coverage of various numerical techniques using time series data, the chapter also provides a very useful discussion on measuring and comparing the effectiveness of the various forecasting techniques.

KEY CONCEPTS AND TERMS

time series analysis: the historical study of long-term trends, seasonal variations and business cycle developments over time. (p. 859)

time series: a set of numerical data that are obtained at regular periods over time. (p. 859)

trend: overall or persistent, long-term upward or downward pattern of movement. (p. 859)

seasonal: fairly regular periodic fluctuations that occur within each 12-month period year after year. (p.861)

cyclical: repeating up-and-down swings or movements through four phases: from peak (prosperity) to contraction (recession) to trough (depression) to expansion (recovery or growth). (p. 860)

irregular: erratic or nonsystematic (random) fluctuations in a time series that exist after taking into account the systematic effects - trend, seasonal and cyclical. (p. 861)

320

classical multiplicative time-series model: (p. 861)

$$Y_i = T_i \times C_i \times I_i \times S_i$$

where Y_i = an observation recorded in time period i

T_i = value of the trend component

C_i = value of the cyclical component

I_i = value of the irregular component

S_i = value of the seasonal component (quarterly or monthly data)

moving averages: consist of a series of arithmetic means computed over time for a chosen period L, such that each mean is calculated for a sequence of observed values having that particular length. (p. 863)

$$MA_i(L) = \frac{1}{L} \sum_{t=(1-L)/2}^{(L-1)/2} Y_{i+t}$$

where L = *an odd number of years*

and $i = \left(\frac{L-1}{2}\right) + 1, \left(\frac{L-1}{2}\right) + 2, \ldots, n - \left(\frac{L-1}{2}\right)$

exponential smoothing: a technique that smooths a time series and provides an impression as to the overall long-term movements in the data. The weights given to the past data decrease exponentially with time. (p. 866) $E_i = WY_i + (1 - W)E_{i-1}$

where E_i = value of the exponentially smoothed series being computed in time period i

E_{i-1} = value of the exponentially smoothed series already computed in time period i-1

Y_i = observed value of the time series in period i

W = subjectively assigned weight or smoothing coefficient (where $0 < W < 1$)

$$W = \frac{2}{L+1}$$

forecasting with exponential smoothing: to use the exponentially weighted moving average for purposes of forecasting, assign the smoothed value in the current period of time (i) as the projected estimate of the observed value of the time series in the following time period ($\hat{Y}_{i+1} = \epsilon_i$). (p. 869)

least squares method for a linear model: a mathematical technique that determines the values of b_0 (intercept) and b_1 (slope) that best fit the observed data. Least-squares refers to the minimization of the squared differences between actual and predicted values

of Y_i. (p. 872)
$$\sum_{i=1}^{n} (Y_i - \hat{Y}_i)^2$$

$$\hat{Y}_i = b_0 + b_1 X_i \qquad sample$$

least squares equations to determine b_0 and b_1: (p. 872)

$$b_1 = \frac{\sum_{i=1}^{n} X_i Y_i - n\overline{X}\overline{y}}{\sum_{i=1}^{n} X_i^2 - n\overline{X}^2}$$

$$b_0 = \overline{Y} - b_1 \overline{X} \quad where \quad \overline{Y} = \frac{\sum_{i=1}^{n} Y_i}{n} \quad and \quad \overline{X} = \frac{\sum_{i=1}^{n} X_i}{n}$$

When the least squares method is used for trend fitting purposes, the X values represent the time component in months quarters, years, etc.. They are usually coded such that the first time period has a code value of zero and the remaining time periods are assigned consecutively increasing numbers 1 through n-1 to ease the computational burden.

quadratic (second degree polynomial) model: used to represent nonlinear trends. (p. 874) A second degree polynomial has the following form:

$$\hat{Y}_i = b_0 + b_1 X_i + b_{11} X_i^2$$

where b_0 = estimated Y intercept

b_1 = estimated linear effect on Y

b_{11} = estimated curvilinear effect on Y

exponential model: used to represent nonlinear trends when a time series appears to be increasing at an increasing rate such that the proportion of change between two consecutive observations is constant. (p. 876)

An exponential trend can be expressed with the following equation:

$$\hat{Y}_i = b_0 b_1^{X_i}$$

where b_0 = estimated Y intercept

$(b_1 - 1)100\%$ = estimated annual compound growth rate (in percent)

If logarithms are taken on both sides of the equation, the following equation results. This equation is in linear form and can be solved using the simple least squares linear regression method described earlier.

$$\log \hat{Y}_i = \log b_0 + X_i \log b_1$$

When using the least squares equation in conjunction with the above equation the log of the Y variable is treated as the dependent variable instead of the Y variable itself.

Holt-Winters method: an extension of the simple exponential smoothing method described earlier where the forecast is adjusted according to the existing trend in the data. (p. 884)

While the simple exponential smoothing method is limited to forecasting one period ahead, the Holt-Winters method can be used to forecast many time periods into the future. Holt-Winters method is comprised of two major components called level and trend. The equations for these components are given below:

$$level = E_i = U(E_{i-1} + T_{i-1}) + (1 - U) Y_i$$
$$trend = T_i = VT_{i-1} + (1 - V) (E_i - E_{i-1})$$

where E_i = level of the smoothed series computed in time period i

E_{i-1} = level of the smoothed series computed in time period i-1

T_i = value of the trend component in time period i

T_{i-1} = value of the trend component in time period i-1

Y_i = observed value of the time series in time period i

U = subjectively assigned smoothing constant (where $0<U<1$)

V   = subjectively assigned smoothing constant (where $0 < V < 1$)

The values obtained for level and trend using the above equations are then combined in the following equation to forecast j periods into the future.

$$\hat{Y}_{n+j} = \epsilon_n + j(T_n)$$

where $\hat{Y}_{(n+j)}$ = forecasted value j years into the future

n = most recent time period

autoregressive model: expresses the observations Y_i in a time series as a function of previous observations $Y_{i-1}, Y_{i-2},...,Y_{i-p}$. (p. 888)

first order autocorrelation: refers to the magnitude of association between consecutive values in a time-series. (p. 888)

pth order autocorrelation: refers to the magnitude of association between values in a time-series that are p periods apart. (p. 888)

The following equations represent first, second, and pth order autoregressive models respectively.

$$Y_i = \omega + \psi_1 Y_{i-1} + \delta_i$$
$$Y_i = \omega + \psi_1 Y_{i-1} + \psi_2 Y_{i-2} + \delta_i$$
$$Y_i = \omega + \psi_1 Y_{i-1} + \psi_2 Y_{i-2} + ... + \psi_p Y_{i-p} + \delta_i$$

where Y_i = observed value of the series at time i

Y_{i-1} = observed value of the series at time i-1

Y_{i-2} = observed value of the series at time i-2

Y_{i-p} = observed value of the series at time i-p

ω = the fixed parameter to be estimated from least squares regression

$\psi_1, \psi_2,..., \psi_p$ = pth autoregression parameter to be estimated from least squares regression analysis

δ_i = random, nonautocorrelated error component (with zero mean and constant variance)

determining appropriateness of the model: test statistic for the highest order autoregressive parameter (p. 890)

324

$$Z = \frac{\hat{\psi}}{S_{\hat{\psi}_p}}$$

where $\hat{\psi}_p$ = the estimate of the highest-order parameter ψ_p in the autoregressive model

$S_{\hat{\psi}_p}$ = the standard deviation of $\hat{\psi}_p$

principle of parsimony: from a set of available forecasting models, selection of the simplest model that can provide adequate, reasonable predictions. (p. 898)

residual: difference between the actual value and the predicted value for a given observation in a time series. (p. 897)

residual analysis: study of the residual plots over n time periods to determine whether the particular model fits the data adequately. (p. 897)

sum of squares of unexplained variation (SSE): measures the magnitude of the residual error based on the sum of squared differences between the actual and predicted values in a given time series. The smaller the SSE the better the fit of the model to the data. (p. 898)

mean absolute deviation (MAD): a measure of the average of the absolute differences between the actual and the predicted values in a given time series. The smaller the MAD the better the fit of the model to the data. (p. 899)

MAD is given by the following equation:

$$MAD = \frac{\sum_{i=1}^{n} |Y_i - \hat{Y}_i|}{n}$$

seasonal index: accounts for the month-to-month or season-to-season fluctuations. (p. 905)

ratios to moving average: isolating seasonal and irregular fluctuations in the series (p. 908)

$$\frac{Y_i}{weighted\ moving\ average_i} = \frac{T_i \cdot S_i \cdot C_i \cdot I_i}{T_i \cdot C_i} = S_i \cdot I_i$$

REVIEW QUESTIONS

1. Compare the two basic approaches to forecasting.

2. What is the basic assumption in time-series analysis? Give examples of how this assumption could be violated.

3. In the computation of moving averages, longer periods of duration smooth the series better than shorter periods. Why aren't all moving averages computed on long periods (over 7 years)?

4. What are the advantages of using the exponential smoothing technique rather than moving averages to smooth a time series?

5. Explain the similarities and differences between simple exponential smoothing and the Holt-Winters model.

6. What approaches are offered in the text as guidelines in the selection of the most appropriate model from a given set of models for prediction purposes. Briefly discuss each of these approaches.

7. Discuss the trade-off between the principle of parsimony and failing to take into account an important behavior of the data.

MULTIPLE CHOICE AND FILL IN QUESTIONS

1. The _____ component in the multiplicative time series model is the only unsystematic factor.

2. When data are obtained quarterly or monthly, the _____ component can be added to the time-series model.

3. In choosing a smoothing coefficient (W), the goal of the analysis is important. If long-term effects are to be predicted, a _____ value for W is suggested and if short-term directions are important, a _____ value of W is recommended.

a) large, small   b) small, large

4. The weighted moving average consists of the _____ and _____ components of the series.

5. The Holt-Winters model can be used to forecast more than one period into the future.

a) true   b) false

6. The Holt-Winters model can be considered an extension of the

a) simple moving averages.

b) simple least squares method.

c) first order autoregressive model.

d) quadratic model.

e) exponential smoothing technique.

7. A form of regression model that matches values of the dependent variable with lagged values of the dependent variable as the explanatory variable is called a(n)

_____.

a) quadratic model   b) exponential model

c) autoregressive model   d) least squares model

e) Holt-Winters model

8. Which one of the following models is the most appropriate for a company that is experiencing an increase in sales, occurring at an increasing rate, such that the percentage growth rate appears to be constant from one year to the next.

a) quadratic model   b) exponential model

c) autoregressive model   d) least squares model

9. A seasonal component refers to any consistent patterns in the data associated with season or month of the year, day of the week or some other period of interest within the year.

a) true   b) false

10. In measuring the magnitude of the residual error, MAD is affected more than SSE by odd, outlying observations.

a) true   b) false

11. The simple moving average method should not be used for forecasting purposes if there is a significant trend in the data.

a) true   b) false

12. In simple exponential smoothing the smaller the smoothing constant, the less forecasted demand will lag behind actual demand.

a) true   b) false

EXERCISES

1. The number of revenue passengers carried by domestic trunk airlines for the years 1987 - 1990 (Jan) are given in the table below. Determine the seasonal index for July and the deseasonalized number of passengers for July 1989. Interpret the meaning of the seasonal index for July.

Year Month	Passengers	13 Month Wgtd Moving Total	Weighted Moving Avg	Ratios to Moving Avg
1987 Jan	24.38			
Feb	25.62			
Mar	32.30			
Apr	31.66			
May	31.17			
Jun	30.57			
Jul	32.21			
Aug	32.70			
Sep	26.07			
Oct	28.27			
Nov	27.48			
Dec	27.48			
1988 Jan	25.47			
Feb	26.36			
Mar	31.91			
Apr	30.01			
May	30.56			
Jun	31.24			
Jul	32.11			
Aug	33.70			
Sep	27.70			

Oct	30.18			
Nov	28.78			
Dec	28.13			
1989 Jan	26.09			
Feb	24.99			
Mar	30.47			
Apr	28.21			
May	29.16			
Jun	31.59			
Jul	31.64			
Aug	33.62			
Sep	27.05			
Oct	30.13			
Nov	28.82			
Dec	28.42			
Jan	29.38			

Source: Standard & Poor's Statistical Service, January 1991

Month	1987	1988	1989	Seasonal Index	Deseason-alized Data
Jul					

2. A government health care official has been assigned to predict the cost of health care for a particular region. The health care costs in billions of dollars is given below.

```
-----------------------------------------------------------------
YEAR:   1  2  3  4  5  6  7  8  9 10 11 12 13 14 15 16 17 18 19 20
-----------------------------------------------------------------
COST:  10 12 15 18 23 26 30 31 36 40 41 40 46 50 63 68 74 76 81 88
-----------------------------------------------------------------
```

a) Plot the time series data.

b) Smooth the data using a three year moving average.

c) Assume that the exponentially smoothed value for the 18th year is 76 and that the smoothing constant W = 0.4. Determine the exponentially smoothed values for the 19th and the 20th years (E_{19} and E_{20}). If exponential smoothing is used for the purposes of forecasting, what would be the forecasted health care costs for the 21st year?

d) Assume that the level of the smoothed series for the 18th year is known to be 73 (E_{18} = 73), and the value of the trend component for the 18th year is 6.0 (T_{18} = 6.0). The selected smoothing constants for the level and trend components are U =.3 and V = .4 respectively. Use the Holt-Winter model and determine the level and trend values for the 19th and the 20th periods. Forecast the cost of health care for the next three years into the future using the level and trend values from the 20th year.

e) Use a statistical computer software package and fit the simple least squares model for this time series data. Express the model and predict the cost of health care for the 21st year.

f) Use a statistical computer software package and fit the quadratic model for this time series data. Express the model and forecast the cost of health care for the 21st year.

g) Use a statistical computer software package and fit the exponential model for this time series data. Express the model and forecast the cost of health care for the 21st year.

h) Use a statistical computer software package and fit the first order autoregressive model for this time series data. How many comparisons would be lost in the development of this autoregressive model? Express the model and predict the cost of health care for the 21st and the 22nd years.

i) Use a statistical computer software package and fit the second order autoregressive model for this time series data. How many comparisons would be lost in the development of this model? Express the model and write an equation to indicate how you would forecast 2 years into the future. Forecast the cost of health care for the 21st and the 22nd years.

j) Test the highest order parameter of the second order autoregressive model (p = 2) for significance at α = .01. If the null hypothesis is not rejected, test the first order parameter of the first order autoregressive model developed in part b. Use α = .01. Carefully state your conclusions.

k) Compare the SSE of the simple linear least squares model with the SSE of the quadratic model. Which one of the two models appear to fit the health care cost data set better? Why is it not appropriate to directly compare the SSE of the exponential model with the SSE of the quadratic model?

3. The following table provides the actual demand and the forecasted demand using the simple linear least squares and the Holt-Winters models.

Actual demand (Y_i)	Forecast using least squares ($\hat{Y}_{i1}$)	Forecast using Holt-Winters ($\hat{Y}_{i2}$)
150	130	180
200	160	205
210	190	230
240	220	255

Compute the mean absolute deviation (MAD) measure of forecast accuracy. Comment on whether these two models are underestimating or overestimating demand. According to the MAD criterion, which of the models provide a better forecast?

ANSWERS TO REVIEW QUESTIONS

1. Qualitative forecasting is subjective and judgmental; important when historical data is not available (i.e., predicting response to a new movie release). Quantitative forecasting makes use of historical data by studying the underlying structure to better predict future occurrences.

2. The basic assumption is that factors that have influenced patterns of activity in the past and present will continue to do so in the future. Violations to this assumption could be caused by the development of new technology, the outbreak of a war, or major cultural changes which alter patterns of buying behavior.

3. The longer the period, the fewer the number of moving average values that can be computed and plotted. To prevent too much missing data, it is usually not desirable to select durations of longer than seven years.

4. Exponential smoothing can be used to obtain short-term forecasts (one period into the future) when long-term trend effect is not apparent. A second advantage is that each forecast is dependent upon all previous forecasts so that all observations are considered in the prediction.

5. The simple exponential smoothing can be an effective method in smoothing a time series. However, it is not as effective for purposes of forecasting if there is a significant trend in the time series. In addition, the exponential smoothing is used to make predictions only one period into the future. The Holt-Winters method can be considered an extension of the simple exponential method. This method can be effective in forecasting particularly if there is a significant upward or downward trend in the data due to its internal trend adjustment mechanism. The Holt-Winters method can also be used to forecast numerous periods into the future.

6. Three approaches offered by the textbook in the selection of the most appropriate model for prediction purposes are:

a) performing residual analysis

b) measuring the magnitude of the residual error

c) using the principle of parsimony

It is important to perform **residual analysis** because random distribution of the residuals around zero indicates a reasonably good fit of the model to the data. Any consistent patterns in a residual plot indicates that the particular model does not fit the data well.

If two or more models are being compared, the residual analysis may not be sufficient to show the magnitude of the unexplained variation (difference between the fitted and the actual values of the time series). In these circumstances SSE (sum of the squared differences between the actual and predicted values) or MAD (mean absolute difference between the actual and predicted values) can be used to compare the relative fit of two or more models. The forecasting model with the smallest SSE or MAD would be considered the most appropriate in terms of minimizing the unexplained variation. The latter of the two is often preferred because the MAD is less influenced by one or two "badly fitting" data points than is the SSE.

If a researcher can't decide among competing forecasting models after using the first two approaches **the principle of parsimony** can be used to make the final decision. According to this principle, the researcher should select the simplest and least cumbersome model that appears to provide a satisfactory result in terms of minimizing the error (SSE or MAD).

7. In one extreme, in an attempt to keep the model simple and sound, a researcher may overlook possibly important variables or a certain type of behavior that exists in the data set. In this situation, using a more sophisticated model may significantly reduce the magnitude of the error. In the other extreme, a researcher may be using a more sophisticated forecasting model unnecessarily. In this situation, using the principle of parsimony, a less sophisticated model would be more appropriate if it does not significantly affect the magnitude of the error.

ANSWERS TO MULTIPLE CHOICE AND FILL IN

1. irregular	7. c
2. seasonal	8. b
3. b	9. a
4. trend, cyclical	10. b
5. a	11. a
6. e	12. b

SOLUTIONS TO EXERCISES

1.

Year Month	Passengers	13 Month Wgtd Moving Total	Weighted Moving Avg	Ratios to Moving Avg
1987 Jan	24.38			
Feb	25.62			
Mar	32.30			
Apr	31.66			
May	31.17			
Jun	30.57			
Jul	32.21	700.91	29.2045	1.1029
Aug	32.70			
Sep	26.07			
Oct	28.27			
Nov	27.48			
Dec	27.48			
1988 Jan	25.47			
Feb	26.36			
Mar	31.91			
Apr	30.01			
May	30.56			
Jun	31.24			
Jul	32.11	712.92	29.7050	1.0810
Aug	33.70			
Sep	27.70			
Oct	30.18			
Nov	28.78			
Dec	28.13			

1989 Jan	26.09			
Feb	24.99			
Mar	30.47			
Apr	28.21			
May	29.16			
Jun	31.59			
Jul	31.64	703.67	29.3196	1.0791
Aug	33.62			
Sep	27.05			
Oct	30.13			
Nov	28.82			
Dec	28.42			
1990 Jan	29.38			

To obtain the 13 month weighted average for July 1987:

$24.38 + 2 (25.62 + 32.30 + \ldots + 27.48) + 25.47 = 700.91$

weighted moving average $= 700.91/24 = 29.02045$

ratio to moving average $= 32.21/29.2045 = 1.1029$

Month	1987	1988	1989	Seasonal Index	Deseason- alized Data
Jul	1.1029	1.0810	1.0791	1.0810	29.2692

The seasonal index = median over 1987, 1988 and 1989 = 1.0810

deseasonalized for July, 1989 $= 31.64/1.0810 = 29.2692$

The seasonal index of 1.0810 means that the number of passengers in July are 8.1% higher than the monthly average.

2. a)

```
     COST
          -
          -
          -                                                              1
          -
     75.0+                                                        1  1
          -                                                   1
          -                                               1
          -
     50.0+                                        1
          -                                    1
          -                             1  1  1
          -                          1
     25.0+                    1  1  1
          -              1  1
          -           1
          -        1
          -  1  1
          +---+---+---+---+---+---+---+---+---+---+
          0       4       8       12      16      20
                              YEAR
```

b)

Year	Health Care Costs	Centered Moving Average
1	10	
2	12	12.333*
3	15	15.000
4	18	18.660
5	23	22.333
6	26	26.333
7	30	29.000
8	31	32.333
9	36	35.667
10	40	39.000
11	41	40.333
12	40	42.333
13	46	45.333
14	50	53.000
15	63	60.333
16	68	68.333
17	74	72.667
18	76	77.000**
19	81	81.667
20	88	

* $\dfrac{10 + 12 + 15}{3} = 12.333$

** $\dfrac{74 + 76 + 81}{3} = 77.000$

c)

$$E_{19} = WY_{19} + (1-W) E_{19-1}$$

$$E_{19} = (.4)(81) + (.6)(76) = 78$$

$$E_{20} = (.4)(88) + (.6)(78) = 82$$

$$\hat{Y}_{21} = E_{20} = 82$$

d)

$$E_{19} = (U)(E_{18} + T_{18}) + (1 - U)(Y_{19})$$
$$= (.3)(73 + 6) + (.7)(81) = 80.4$$

$$T_{19} = (V)(T_{18}) + (1 - V)(E_{19} - E_{18})$$
$$= (.4)(6) + (1-.4)(80.4 - 73) = 6.84$$

$$E_{20} = (.3)(80.4 + 6.84) + (.7)(88) = 87.772$$

$$T_{20} = (.4)(6.84) + (.6)(87.772 - 80.4) = 7.159$$

$$\hat{Y}_{21} = E_{20} + (1) T_{20}$$

$$\hat{Y}_{21} = 87.772 + (1)(7.159) = 94.9$$

$$\hat{Y}_{22} = E_{20} + (2)(T_{20})$$

$$\hat{Y}_{22} = 87.772 + (2)(7.159) = 102.1$$

$$\hat{Y}_{23} = E_{20} + (3)(T_{20})$$

$$\hat{Y}_{23} = 87.772 + (3)(7.159) = 109.2$$

e)

Predictor	Coef	Stdev	t-ratio	p
Constant	1.132	2.061	0.55	0.590
C1	4.0256	0.1721	23.40	0.000

$s = 4.437$ R-sq = 96.8%   R-sq(adj) = 96.6%

Analysis of Variance

SOURCE	DF	SS	MS	F	p
Regression	1	10776	10776	547.39	0.000
Error	18	354	20		
Total	19	11131			

342

Simple least squares model: $\hat{Y}_i = 1.132 + (4.0256)X_i$

origin = year 1, X units = 1 year

$\hat{Y}_{21} = 1.132 + 4.0256(21) = 85.67$

f)

```
Predictor        Coef        Stdev      t-ratio         p
Constant        9.535        2.175        4.38       0.000
C1             1.7337       0.4770        3.63       0.002
C4            0.10914      0.02206        4.95       0.000

s = 2.923       R-sq = 98.7%     R-sq(adj) = 98.5%
```

Analysis of Variance

```
SOURCE       DF         SS          MS          F         p
Regression    2     10985.5      5492.8      642.83    0.000
Error        17       145.3         8.5
Total        19     11130.8
```

Quadratic model: $\hat{Y}_i = 9.535 + (1.7337)X_i + (.10914)X_i^2$

$\hat{Y}_{21} = 9.535 + 1.7337(21) + .10914(21^2)$

$\hat{Y}_{21} = 94.07$

g)

```
Predictor        Coef        Stdev      t-ratio         p
Constant      1.07342      0.02618       41.01       0.000
C1           0.046456     0.002185       21.26       0.000

s = 0.05635     R-sq = 96.2%     R-sq(adj) = 96.0%
```

Analysis of Variance

```
SOURCE       DF         SS          MS          F         p
Regression    1      1.4352      1.4352      451.99    0.000
Error        18      0.0572      0.0032
Total        19      1.4923
```

Exponential model: $\log \hat{Y}_i = 1.07342 + (.046456)X_i$

$$\log \hat{Y}_{21} = 1.07342 + (.046456)(21)$$

$\log \hat{Y}_{21} = 2.04899 \quad \hat{Y}_{21} = \text{antilog } 2.04899 = 111.942$

or

$b_0 = \text{antilog } 1.07342 = 11.8418$

$b_1 = \text{antilog } .046456 = 1.1129$

$\hat{Y}_i = 11.8418(1.1129)^{X_i}$

$\hat{Y}_{21} = 11.8418 (1.1129)^{21}$

$\hat{Y}_{21} = 111.942$

h)

```
Predictor        Coef        Stdev      t-ratio          p
Constant         2.370       1.402         1.69       0.109
C6               1.04226     0.03015      34.57       0.000

s = 2.866       R-sq = 98.6%      R-sq(adj) = 98.5%

Analysis of Variance

SOURCE      DF          SS          MS         F         p
Regression   1        9816.9      9816.9    1195.03    0.000
Error       17         139.7         8.2
Total       18        9956.5
```

One comparison would be lost in the development of this autoregressive model.

First order autoregressive model: $\hat{Y}_i = 2.37 + 1.04266(Y_{i-1})$

$\hat{Y}_{21} = 2.37 + 1.04226(88)$

$\hat{Y}_{21} = 94.088$

$\hat{Y}_{22} = 2.37 + 1.04266(94.088)$

$\hat{Y}_{22} = 100.47$

i)

```
Predictor        Coef        Stdev      t-ratio           p
Constant        4.314        1.116        3.87        0.002
C8              0.5634       0.2349       2.40        0.030
C9              0.4768       0.2410       1.98        0.067

s = 1.676       R-sq = 99.5%      R-sq(adj) = 99.5%
```

Analysis of Variance

```
SOURCE          DF          SS          MS          F            p
Regression       2        8821.0      4410.5     1570.55     0.000
Error           15          42.1         2.8
Total           17        8863.1
```

Second order autoregressive model:

Two comparisons would be lost in the development of this model.

$\hat{Y}_i = 4.314 + .5634(Y_{i-1}) + .4768(Y_{i-2})$

The general form of the equation to forecast two years ahead would be expressed as follows:

$\hat{Y}_{n+2} = 4.314 + .5634(\hat{Y}_{n+1}) + .4768(Y_n)$

$\hat{Y}_{21} = 4.314 + .5634(88) + .4768(81)$

$\hat{Y}_{21} = 92.514$

$\hat{Y}_{22} = 4.314 + .5634(92.514) + .4768(88)$

$\hat{Y}_{22} = 98.395$

j. H_0: $\psi_2 = 0$ (The second order parameter is zero)

  H_1: $\psi_2 \neq 0$ (The parameter ψ_2 is significantly meaningful)

Reject H_0 if $Z > Z_{(.01)/2}$ or $Z < -Z_{(.01)/2}$

$$Z_{(.01)/2} = Z_{.005} = 2.58 \qquad\qquad Z = \frac{\psi_2}{S_{\psi_2}} = \frac{.4768}{.241} = 1.98$$

Since $1.98 < 2.58$, we may not reject H_0, and conclude that the second order parameter of the autoregressive model is not significantly important and can be deleted.

Returning to our first-order autoregressive model obtained in part (h):

H_0: $\psi_1 = 0$ (The first order parameter is zero)

H_1: $\psi_2 \neq 0$ (The parameter ψ_1 is significantly meaningful)

Reject H_0 if $Z > Z_{(.01)/2}$ or $Z < -Z_{(.01)/2}$

$$Z_{(.01)/2} = Z_{.005} = 2.58 \qquad\qquad Z = \frac{\psi_1}{S_{\psi_1}} = \frac{1.0423}{.03015} = 34.57$$

Since $34.57 > 2.58$, we reject H_0, and conclude that the first order parameter of the autoregressive model is significantly important.

k) $SSE_{quadratic} = 145.3 \qquad\qquad SSE_{simple} = 354$

  The quadratic model appears to fit the health care cost data set better. It is not appropriate to directly compare the SSE of the exponential model with the SSE of the quadratic model because the two respective SSE values are in different metrics.

3.

Actual Demand Y_i	Linear $\hat{Y}_i$	e_i	Holt-Winters $\hat{Y}_i$	e_i
150	130	20	180	-30
200	160	40	205	-5
210	190	20	230	-20
240	220	20	255	-15
Absolute Sum		100		70
MAD	100/4 = 25		70/4 = 17.5	

The linear model is underestimating demand and the Holt-Winters model is overestimating demand. According to the MAD criteria, the Holt-Winters model provides a better forecast than the linear model.

APPENDIX A

REVIEW OF ARITHMETIC AND ALGEBRA

To solve the problems and exercises presented in this text, a good understanding of basic arithmetic and algebra is essential. The following quiz should be taken at the beginning of the semester as a self-evaluation of basic math skills.

EXERCISES

PART I Fill in the correct answer.

1. $\dfrac{1}{\dfrac{3}{4}} =$

2. $.3^2 =$

3. $1 + \dfrac{3}{4} =$

4. $\left(\dfrac{1}{4}\right)^3 =$

5. $\dfrac{2}{5} =$ *(decimal)*

6. $1 - (-.4) =$

7. $3 \times .2 \times (-4) =$

8. $\left(\dfrac{1}{3}\right) \times \left(\dfrac{3}{4}\right) =$

9. $\dfrac{1}{100} + \dfrac{1}{300} =$

10. $\sqrt{25} =$

PART II Select the correct answer

1. If a + b = c, then b =

    (a) c + a

    (b) c - a

    (c) $\dfrac{c}{a}$

    (d) None of the above.

2. If x = yz, then z =

    (a) xy

    (b) $\dfrac{y}{x}$

    (c) $\dfrac{x}{y}$

    (d) None of the above.

3. x^0 =

    (a) x

    (b) 1

    (c) 0

    (d) None of the above.

4. $(x^4)\,(x^3)$ =

    (a) x^{12}

    (b) x^7

    (c) x^1

    (d) None of the above.

5. a(b - c) =

    (a) ab - ac

    (b) ab - c

    (c) $\dfrac{b-c}{a}$

    (d) None of the above.

6. $\dfrac{z+y}{x}$ =

    (a) $\left(\dfrac{z}{x}\right) + y$

    (b) $\left(\dfrac{z}{x}\right) + \left(\dfrac{y}{x}\right)$

    (c) $z + \left(\dfrac{y}{x}\right)$

    (d) None of the above.

7. $\dfrac{z}{y+x}$ =

    (a) $\left(\dfrac{z}{y}\right) + \left(\dfrac{z}{x}\right)$

    (b) $\left(\dfrac{z}{y}\right) + \left(\dfrac{1}{x}\right)$

    (c) $\dfrac{z}{yx}$

    (d) None of the above.

8. If x = 8, y = 3, z = 2, w = 24,

   then $\dfrac{xy - z^2}{w}$ =

   (a) .833

   (b) .9166

   (c) 1.166

   (d) None of the above.

9. $\dfrac{6x^8}{3x^4}$ =

   (a) 2

   (b) 2x

   (c) $2x^2$

   (d) None of the above.

10. $\sqrt{\dfrac{a}{b}}$ =

   (a) $\dfrac{\sqrt{b}}{\sqrt{a}}$

   (b) $\dfrac{\sqrt{ab}}{\sqrt{b}}$

   (c) $\dfrac{\sqrt{a}}{\sqrt{b}}$

   (d) None of the above.

350

ANSWERS TO QUIZ

Part I

1. 4/3	6. 1.4
2. .09	7. -2.4
3. 7/4	8. 1/4
4. 1/64	9. 1/75
5. .40	10. 5

Part II

1. b	6. b
2. c	7. d
3. b	8. a
4. b	9. d
5. a	10. c

Appendix B

Summation Notation

Many formulas in the textbook use the symbol Σ (the capital greek letter sigma) to denote the summation of terms. Students need to develop a basic understanding of how this symbol is used in expressing various statistical expressions.

The following examples illustrate the use of this notation.

Let $X_1 = 7$, $X_2 = 5$, $X_3 = 6$, $X_4 = 2$.

In order to express the sum of these four variables

$(X_1 + X_2 + X_3 + X_4 = 7 + 5 + 6 + 2)$ in a summary form, we can use the summation notation.

$$\sum_{i=1}^{4} X_i = X_1 + X_2 + X_3 + X_4 = 7 + 5 + 6 + 2 = 20$$

The subscript i is the index used to distinguish the different values assumed by the variable X from each other. The left side of the equation can be expressed as the summation of X_i going from 1 to 4. The expression $i = 1$, below the Σ shows the beginning of the summation, while the number above the Σ indicates the end of the summation. Since the summation begins with $i = 1$, the first term is given by replacing X_i with X_1, the second term is given by replacing X_i with X_2, the third term is given by replacing X_i with X_3, etc. Since the summation for the above example goes from one to four, the last term in the sum is X_4.

In general, the letter "n" is used above the Σ instead of a specific number to provide the following general expression of the summation notation.

$$\sum_{i=1}^{n} X_i$$

expression of summation notation with squared terms: Following are the two basic properties of the summation notation involving squared expressions.

$$\sum_{i=1}^{n} X_i^2 = X_1^2 + X_2^2 + X_3^2 + \ldots + X_n^2$$

$$\left(\sum_{i=1}^{n} X_i\right)^2 = (X_1 + X_2 + X_3 + \ldots + X_n)^2$$

Note that we are summing the squared values of the variable X in the first expression. In the second expression, all of the values of the variable X are first summed and then the sum is squared.

expression of summation notation with constant terms: Let the letter "a" without a subscript denote a constant instead of a variable. The following are two basic properties of the summation notation involving constants:

$$\sum_{i=1}^{n} a X_i = aX_1 + aX_2 + aX_3 + \ldots$$

$$= a\left(\sum_{i=1}^{n} X_i\right)$$

$$\sum_{i=1}^{n} a = a + a + a + \ldots + a = na$$

The first of the above expressions shows that the sum of the cross products of each variable X_i with the constant "a" is the same as multiplying the constant "a" with the sum of the values of the variable X_i. The second expression demonstrates that summing n values of a constant is the same as multiplying that constant by n.

expression of summation notation for two variables: Up to this point, the properties of summation notation involved a single variable. However, in statistics, many techniques deal with more than one variable. Therefore, it is important to understand how the summation notation is used for two or more variables. The following expression is a simple rule for two variables.

$$\sum_{i=1}^{n} (X_i + Y_i) = (X_1 + Y_1) + (X_2 + Y_2) + \ldots + (X_n - Y_n)$$

$$\sum_{i=1}^{n} (X_i + Y_i) = \sum_{i=1}^{n} X_i + \sum_{i=1}^{n} Y_i$$

The following summation notation can be used to describe sum of the cross products for two variables.

$$\sum_{i=1}^{n} X_i Y_i = X_1 Y_1 + X_2 Y_2 + \ldots + X_n Y_n$$

double summation notation: some statistical formulas require the use of double summation notation. One such example involves summing a variable over two different categories:

$$\sum_{i=1}^{n} \sum_{j=1}^{m} X_{ij}$$

Notice in this case, the variable X has two subscripts i and j. The subscript i is the index used to distinguish the variable with respect to the first category, while j is the index used to distinguish the variable with respect to the second category. In the above example of double summation, the subscript i, denotes the first category which ranges from 1 to n, and the subscript j denotes the second category which ranges from 1 to m. The above example of double summation can also be written as:

$$\sum_{i=1}^{n} \left(\sum_{j=1}^{m} X_{ij} \right) = \sum_{j=1}^{n} X_{1j} + \sum_{j=1}^{m} X_{2j} + \ldots + \sum_{j=1}^{m} X_{nj}$$

where:

$$\sum_{j=1}^{m} X_{1j} = X_{11} + X_{12} + X_{13} + \ldots + X_1 m$$

$$\sum_{j=1}^{m} X_{2j} = X_{21} + X_{22} + X_{23} + \ldots + X_2 m$$

EXERCISES

1. Let $Y_1 = 5$, $Y_2 = 4$, $Y_3 = 7$, $X_1 = 10$, $X_2 = 15$, $X_3 = 9$, and determine the numerical values associated with the following expressions.

a) $\sum_{i=1}^{3} X_i + \sum_{i=1}^{3} Y_i$

b) $\sum_{i=1}^{3} X_i Y_i$

c) $\sum_{i=1}^{3} (X_i - Y_i)$

2. The following table provides the values of the variable X classified according to two categories.

		Category 2			
		j = 1	j = 2	j = 3	j = 4
Category 1	i = 1	4	7	3	9
	i = 2	8	5	2	6
	i = 3	5	4	1	8

Let the constant c = 5, and determine the numerical values associated with the following expressions.

a)

$\sum_{i=1}^{3} X_{i1}$

b)

$\sum_{j=1}^{4} X_{2j} + \sum_{j=1}^{4} X_{3j} + \sum_{i=1}^{3} X_{i2}$

c)

$$\sum_{i=1}^{3} X_{i2} X_{i3}$$

d)

$$\sum_{i=2}^{3} \sum_{j=1}^{4} X_{ij}$$

e)

$$\left(\sum_{i=1}^{3} \sum_{j=1}^{4} X_{ij} \right)^2$$

f)

$$\sum_{i=1}^{3} \sum_{j=1}^{4} X_{ij}^2$$

g)

$$\sum_{j=1}^{4} (X_{2j} + X_{3j})^3$$

h)

$$\sum_{i=1}^{3} X_{i2}^2 + \sum_{i=1}^{3} X_{i4}^2$$

i)

$$\sum_{i=1}^{3} (X_{i2} + X_{i4})^2$$

j)

$$\sum_{i=2}^{3} (X_{i1}^2 - c)^2 + c \left(\sum_{j=2}^{3} X_{2j} \right)^2 - c$$

k) Verify using the numbers in this problem that:

$$\sum_{i=1}^{3} cX_{i3} = c \sum_{i=1}^{3} X_{i3}$$

l)

$$\sum_{j=1}^{4} \frac{X_{1j}}{X_{3j}}$$

m)

$$\frac{\sum_{j=1}^{4} X_{1j}}{\sum_{j=1}^{4} X_{3j}}$$

3. Write the following terms using summation notation:

a) $5X_1Y_1 + 5X_2Y_2 + 5X_3Y_3 + 5X_4Y_4$

b)

$$\frac{(X_1 + X_2 + X_3 + X_4 + X_5)^2}{(Y_1^2 + Y_2^2 + Y_3^2 + Y_4^2)}$$

c)

$$\frac{3(a - X_1)^2 + 3(a - X_2)^2 + 3(a - X_3)^2}{(X_1^2 a) + (X_2^2 a) + (X_3^2 a)}$$

4. Write out the individual terms without using summation notation for each of the following expressions. Do not simplify the algebra.

a)

$$\frac{\sum_{i=1}^{3} (X_i + Y_i)^2}{C}$$

b)

$$\frac{\left(\sum_{i=1}^{4} X_i\right)^2 - c\sum_{i=1}^{4} X_i^2}{\sum_{i=1}^{3} \frac{X_i}{Y_i}}$$

c)

$$\left(\sum_{i=2}^{4} X_i\right)^2 - \sum_{i=2}^{4} X_i Y_i^2$$

d)

$$\sum_{i=1}^{3} \sum_{j=1}^{2} X_{ij}^2$$

SOLUTIONS TO EXERCISES

1.

a) $16 + 34 = 50$

b) $(5)(10) + (4)(15) + (7)(9) = 50 + 60 + 63 = 173$

c) $(5-10) + (4-15) + (7-9) = (-5) + (-11) + (-2) = -18$

2.

a) $\quad 4 + 8 + 5 = 17$

b) $\quad (8 + 5 + 2 + 6) + (5 + 4 + 1 + 8) + (7 + 5 + 4) = 55$

c) $\quad (7 * 3) + (5 * 2) + (4 * 1) = 35$

d) $\quad (8 + 5 + 2 + 6 + 5 + 4 + 1 + 8) = 39$

e) $\quad (4 + 7 + 3 + 9 + 8 + 5 + 2 + 6 + 5 + 4 + 1 + 8)^2 = (62)^2 = 3844$

f) $\quad 4^2 + 7^2 + 3^2 + 9^2 + 8^2 + 5^2 + 2^2 + 6^2 + 5^2 + 4^2 + 1^2 + 8^2 = 390$

g) $\quad (8 + 5)^3 + (5 + 4)^3 + (2 + 1)^3 + (6 + 8)^3 = 2197 + 729 + 27 + 2744 = 5697$

h) $\quad (7^2 + 5^2 + 4^2) + (9^2 + 6^2 + 8^2) = 271$

i) $\quad (7 + 9)^2 + (5 + 6)^2 + (4 + 8)^2 = 256 + 121 + 144 = 521$

j) $\quad (8^2 - 5)^2 + (5 - 5)^2 + 5(5 + 2)^2 - 5 = (59)^2 + 5(7)^2 - 5 = 3721$

k) $\quad 5(3) + 5(2) + 5(1) = 5(3 + 2 + 1) = 30$

l)

$$\frac{4}{5} + \frac{7}{4} + \frac{3}{1} + \frac{9}{8} = 6.675$$

m)

$$\frac{4 + 7 + 3 + 9}{5 + 4 + 1 + 8)} = \frac{23}{18} = 1.277$$

3.

a)

$$\sum_{i=1}^{4} 5X_i Y_i \quad or \quad 5\sum_{i=1}^{4} X_i Y_i$$

b)

$$\frac{\left(\sum_{i=1}^{5} X_i\right)^2}{\sum_{i=1}^{5} Y_i^2}$$

c)

$$\frac{3\sum_{i=1}^{3} (a - X_i)^2}{a\sum_{i=1}^{3} X_i^2}$$

4. a)

$$\frac{(X_1 + Y_1)^2 + (X_2 + Y_2)^2 + (X_3 + Y_3)^2}{c}$$

b)

$$\frac{(X_1 + X_2 + X_3 + X_4)^2 (cX_1^2 + cX_2^2 + cX_3^2 + cX_4^2)}{\frac{X_1}{Y_1} + \frac{X_2}{Y_2} + \frac{X_3}{Y_3}}$$

c)

$$(X_2 + X_3 + X_4)^2 - (X_2 Y_2^2) + (X_3 Y_3^2) + (X_4 Y_4^2)$$

d)

$$X_{11}{}^2 + X_{12}{}^2 + X_{21}{}^2 + X_{22}{}^2 + X_{31}{}^2 + X_{32}{}^2$$